Disclaimers

Adults On

This book contains **graphic sexual content:** images, cartoons, and stories.

All characters are 18 years of age or older. All characters are consenting,

"All scenarios are fictional and show no real people or events. Any similarities between persons, characters, names, and/or institutions, living or dead, depicted in this book are purely coincidental, satire, or artistic commentary." Language from Cherry Comics.

You must be 18 or older to read.

This Book Could Have Errors!

I did my best, but this book may have errors, may not apply to you, be unclear, be outdated, or you could understand it differently than I intended. Sex is also nuanced, and each situation is different. This book would be so long if I tried to go through every nuance. I have a longer version with more nuances.

"I and anyone associated with this book shall not be held liable or responsible for any loss, damage, injury, or ailment, etc. caused or alleged to be caused, directly or indirectly, by the information or lack of information contained in this book." This disclaimer language is from a sex ed book I enjoyed, The Guide to Getting It On. (Joannides, 2017-2018). Talk to your healthcare provider to ask questions and confirm understanding.

Money-back guarantee: This book isn't for everyone. My writing, voice, content, editing, illustration choices, etc. If you hate this and want a refund, mail me a proof of purchase and the book, and I'll send you a refund. Email me for my current address: harry@asexed.com

Grammar: I intend for this book to feel like a conversation. So, it's not always grammatically correct. If you notice anything confusing or glaring, please email me. I use "they" as singular in addition plural.

Just the Tips with Cherry

From asking to ass licking to aftercare. A how-to book focusing on communication before, during, and after sex.

Written by Harry Lindner
Edited by Julie DiNuoscio, MA, LPC
Consultant: Alley Schottenstein, PhD

Illustrations from Cherry Comics
by Larry Welz originally published 1982-2000
Used with permission.

Library of Congress Control Number:2019917433
ISBN: 9781733138529
Most Confused and Improved Press
Cincinnati, Columbus, and Wyoming, Ohio

Front cover art from the back cover of Cherry Comics #16.
Back cover art from Cherry #6 Page 26.

This book contains the highlights of Harry Lindner's longer sex education book. That one has more stories, explanations, and topics. If you like this book and want more, check that one out. It's yet to be published, but I can send you an advanced copy if you want. Just email me: harry@asexed.com.

The publishing press name, **Most Confused and Improved Press** comes from two awards I won in high school: most confused (from senior awards) and most improved (from my ultimate frisbee team). These describe my life:

- People believing that I am confused.
- Me improving with practice.

Table of Contents

How to read this book:

Feel free to read it in order or skip to the chapter you care about.
If you are confused, google your question, email me, or post on the forum at asexed.com.

Who is this book for?

This is book is for all adults who are interested in sexual activity. It is written for people who are new to sex or never learned. I believe that is most adults.

Acknowledgments

Thank you

- Jon Branfman, PhD for edits, content suggestions, and improvements.
- More people. Lots more people. I have gotten help from countless friends, family, and acquaintances.
- If you want your name added here, let me know. ☺ If you helped or read this then send me feedback, I want to add your name here.

Introduction

I wrote this book because when I went to have sex, I didn't know what I was doing: "How do we start kissing?" "How do I go from kissing to touching?" "How do I actually have sex?" "How do I end it?" "What do I do after?" I wrote this book to answer those questions.

The point of this book is **good sex = communication + caring about yourself and your partner**. Good sex is sex that is enjoyable for both partners: consensual, caring, fun, and meets the needs and most of the wants of each partner. Caring is an attitude choice you bring. Communication is a few actions. I help with this by suggesting topics and sentence stems for you to use.

The information included comes from my experiences, reading other's writing, conversations and informational interviews, and sex events.

I assume you want sex, have an incomplete idea of what you are doing, might feel awkward talking about it, and want to improve. I assume being good at sex is learned, and most sex educations fail at teaching good sex.

How my book is different:

If we were learning soccer and only learned anatomy and injuries, we would be pretty shitty soccer players. If a better soccer program taught us about shin pads, we still wouldn't know how to play soccer. That's what we have now for sex ed in America: mostly anatomy, STIs / pregnancy, and condoms. While some of the information is factual, it doesn't include 'how-to have sex' or how-to make it enjoyable.

I teach sex like coaches coach soccer: telling you how to play it: the rules, players, plays, and field.

Book Limitations

I am an individual with unique experiences. To broaden my understanding, I sought the help of people different from me – reading their work, listening to their stories, and hearing their feedback. That said, this work will still be incomplete, not the only way to do things, have errors, and will be outdated. Understanding sex, humans, and communication is an ever-growing and changing space.

Sometimes I use gendered pronouns when referring to people with a penis or vulva. I do this for brevity and clarity of writing. Just because someone has a vulva doesn't mean they identify as a woman. Same with penis and man. If you want or need to learn more, read My Gender Workbook or Gender Outlaws by Kate Bornstein. If you are unsure of what pronoun to use with someone, ask them, "what are your preferred pronouns?"

Communication can be hard

Throughout this book, I suggest you talk to your partner. That can be hard. I suggest you talk about your feelings, needs, wants, any STIs, pregnancy plans or prevention, romantic life, and sex life. Most people aren't raised to ask for what they want, set boundaries, talk about their feelings and needs, and talk about sex.

Additionally, I ask you to ask your partner about their feelings, needs, and wants. I ask you to ask them for feedback on your sex. Try to listen without interrupting or judging. That can be hard as you'll feel things based on what they said or have questions and want to share. Save your questions and feelings until they are done talking. Repeat back what they said to confirm your understanding. Believe them. Then ask your questions and share your feelings.

All of that is part of good sex. Communication takes practice, time, and energy. If you practice communication with your partners, I imagine you'll have more, enjoyable sex.

Cherry #12, Page 2.

Section I: Before Sex

Chapter 1. How to initiate sex

Question 1. "Would you like a kiss?" (Covering consent, boundaries, goals, desires, intentions, etc. – Clarifying which acts you'll do.)

Question 2. "Do you know if you have any STIs?" (and sexual history.)

Question 3. "What kind of birth control are we using?" (if needed)

Question 4. "What are your relationship intentions?"

Chapters 2 – 6: Body prep and parts

Chapter 1. Initiating Sexual Activity

To initiate, I ask. I usually do this in private with my romantic partner(s). To get a romantic partner, I ask. I usually do this by meeting people at events, in class, in public, through friends, at parties, anywhere I go, or dating apps.

In preparing for meeting people, I practice honesty with myself and others through my words and actions. I care about myself, work on my passions, say positive things to myself about myself (like "I can handle this"), keep a positive mental attitude (like "things will go well"), believe I am attractive, and believe people I am attracted to - are attracted to me.

When I meet people, I ask them about themselves with genuine curiosity (Carnegie, 1936) and ask them what I want to know (Authentic Relating Games Night, 2016). I share honestly about myself (Manson, 2011). Doing these builds friendships. For the people I am attracted to, I ask if they want to hang out or go on a date.

"I enjoyed chatting with you, would you like to do it again / go on a date?

If they say "yes" and we hang out again, I continue connecting through curiosity and sharing. If I enjoy them and feel attraction, I let them know:

"I enjoy spending time with you, and I'm attracted to you." I ask if they are into me, "Are you attracted to me?" or "Do you feel the same?"

If they say, "yes," they're likely into me. I then may initiate sexual activity, asking without expectation or demand:

"I'd like to kiss you. Would you like that?"

If they say "yes," I'll ask a few more questions before actually kissing: the **four questions** of pre-sexual activity, covered in the next four chapters.

If they said "no" to feeling attracted to me, they probably aren't into me, and I won't ask to kiss. I'll say, "thank you." They may feel awkward now. I might ask if they want to keep hanging out. If they said "yes" to being attracted to me, but "no" to kissing, I say "thank you" and might ask, "what would you like to do now?" If they waver (saying, "ummm," "hmmm," or anything but a confident "yes"), I take that as a "no" and ask if they want to talk about it. I only proceed if they can verbally say "yes – I want to kiss."

Chapter 2. Question 1: "Can I kiss you?"

"Can I give you a hug?" "What do you want to do?" "What don't you want to do?" "What are your sex goals?" "I want to {your desires}. Are you into that?"

These questions ask about consent, boundaries, goals, desires, intentions, etc. The goal of these questions, as with the others, is to connect honestly with your partner: to understand your partner and to be vulnerable – sharing yourself. You want honesty from them, and they want it from you. You should also want to be honest with them (asking for what you want is the best way to get what you want) and if they're not into it, you want to know that so you can find someone who is or have that expectation that you won't be doing that. Practically, this question clarifies if and which sex acts you will do together.

Story 1 Analogy

You're hanging out with your friend and you feel hungry. You ask if they want to get food. They say sure and you discuss where to eat.

> "I had Chinese buffet for lunch. I'd be open to pizza or a burger."
>
> "I could do pizza. Would you want to go to that one place nearby?
>
> "Sure."

You agree on a place. Then you go there and enjoy yourselves.

That's how consent works: discuss desires, boundaries, and then see if you can agree. Only proceed if you agree.

"**Consent** means verbally asking and verbally giving or denying consent for all levels of sexual behavior," (SOPP, 2018). That includes hugging, kissing, undressing, touching, oral sex, vaginal sex, anal sex, and rough play.

Before you engage in any sex act with someone (including hugging or pats on the back), you need their permission to do it.

Here are some potential replies you may receive when you ask for consent:

1. "Yes" or an enthusiastic "yes" "Yes, I want to kiss also."

2. Hesitant "yes": "Uhhhhh, sure / yea? / ok/ I guess so?" If it sounds like a question, it's not a "yes."
3. "Maybe..." "Uhhhh.... I'm not sure..." "mmmmmmmmmmmmmmm..."
4. A confident "no." "No thank you."
5. "No, but... ________." / "No, but we can lie next to each other."

Only with a confident or enthusiastic "yes" can you do the sex act. If they say (5) "No, but..." that means they are offering an alternative and you get to decide if you want to do that. If they say an unclear response (2 or 3), that is likely a "no" and they feel awkward saying it. Even if it's not a confident "no" (4), you can only proceed if you get an enthusiastic "YES!" You can ask more questions or suggest less intense alternatives to see how they feel. You can also ask them, "you don't sound confident about that 'yes.' What's up with that?" and then let them share.

Don't 'Just go for it.'

When people don't ask for consent (which happens), they:

1. Wait for their partner to initiate sexual activity.
2. Send ambiguous nonverbal signals they are attracted to someone in hopes that crush initiates sexual activity. Examples are sitting/standing close to their crush (like knees / shoulders touching), hanging out with / talking to frequently, long eye contact, lots of smiling.)
3. Avoid the person they are interested in.
4. **'Just go for it**,' which is initiating sexual activity without asking. It often looks like leaning in and kissing someone or giving them a hug without permission. Their partner may not have wanted that.
5. Drink alcohol or use drugs as an excuse or removal of responsibility for their desires and actions. "Oh, I was drunk, so it wasn't my fault."

The first 3 don't work well to get sex. The last two are unethical. They encourage a culture of silence which produces bad sex, regret, remorse, and misunderstandings. Later, I discuss alcohol and drugs with sex

Story 2 Comparing Nonverbal Initiations to a High Five

When you want a high five, you raise your hand, palm facing the person you want to high five. You're offering them to clap your hand. If they accept, they raise their hand and clap yours.

You don't 'just go for it' and smack their hand. You don't grab their hand and clap it to yours. You don't force someone into a high five or get drunk then hit their hand. You ask sober while they are sober. They choose if they want it.

The same thing applies with kissing or other sex acts. **Don't just lean in and kiss them (or touch, hug, lightly caress their arm / their body, grab their boob, butt, etc.).** Ask first before any touch – even hugs or pats on the back.

Consent has all of these properties:

1. Ask before you touch (or kiss, undress, suck, or fuck). Even if it's just a hug or pat on the back b/c (because) they may not want your touch.
2. No one has to touch, hug, or do sex acts with anyone. This includes family. If you force a kid to hug or kiss a relative, you're indicating that consent doesn't always matter, and they don't always have control over their own body. That sometimes they have to do what other's want with their body. That's just not true and goes against **agency:**

   People get to choose what happens to their body.

3. Consent starts with an ask for permission to do something b/c otherwise it isn't clear if you are requesting anything. You have to verbally ask to be clear. They may not be clear about your nonverbals.
4. To proceed, you need a "yes." If you get a "no" or "maybe," say "thank you for your honesty." Ask if they still want to hang out. They may want space now.
5. To proceed, the reply has to be a confident or enthusiastic "yes."
   a. If it's a wavering "yes" or an unsure "ok?" or just a flat "fine," then it's a "fuck no." 'If it's not a "fuck yes," it's a "fuck no."' (House of Bacchus , 2018)

6. Consent is needed for each sex act: kissing to touching to undressing to kissing other body parts to fucking. You need consent for each one.
7. Consent is needed for each change of position: on-top, doggie, spooning, on-bottom...
8. Consent is needed for each time you have sex: each session or instance.
9. Consent can be given or removed at any point during any sex act.
10. Consent is only good for the person it's given to, i.e. not a friend.
11. Consent can only happen when you are both sober and awake.
12. Consent requires honesty and believing your partner.
13. Consent can be pre-permission for specific actions or a set of actions. This is called **blanket consent**. I still ask for most new sex acts and I only view this as good for one instance of sex.
14. Affirmative consent, meaning a "yes," is the only real consent (as opposed to nonverbal consent – because you don't actually know if they are consenting without a "yes.")
15. The tone of asking for consent is curious and caring. "*Do you* want to kiss? I genuinely want to know and I'm ok if you say "no."
16. Consent is uncoerced and unpressured.
17. Consent is informed: STI status, other relationships, pregnancy plans...
18. Consent builds. You may start off with a less physically intimate ask, "do you want to kiss?" before you ask, "do you want your ass licked?"
19. Consent is iterative: you ask more than once over time to learn more about yourself and your partner. I generally ask about kissing before asking about sex goals, but it depends on each person and situation.
20. Consent and desires change over time. In long term relationships, you will both change, and so will your desires.

Here is an analogy to help you understand consent:

Story 3 $5 dollar analogy

Quoted directly without edits from (Rawji, 2016).

If you ask me for $5, and I'm too drunk to say yes or no, it's not okay to then go take $5 out of my purse... Just because I didn't say no.

If you put a gun to my head to get me to give you $5, you still stole $5. Even if I physically handed you $5.

If I let YOU borrow $5, that doesn't give the right for your FRIEND to take $5 out of my purse.

"But you gave him some, why can't I?"

If you steal $5 and I can't prove it in court, that does NOT mean you didn't steal $5.

Just because I gave you $5 in the past, doesn't mean I have to give you $5 in the future.

Replace "borrow $5" with "have sex" and you have the analogy.

Point of story: You need a "yes" to proceed with a sex act.

- Being drunk isn't a "yes." Silence isn't a "yes."

- Getting a "yes" with the threat of violence isn't consent.

- A "yes" to a friend doesn't mean you can use that "yes."

- If no one else is around, that doesn't mean it's ok to do it.

- A "yes" yesterday doesn't mean "yes" today. A "yes" can change to "no," "pause," or "not this anymore" at any time – and that's ok.

Will asking for consent ruin the mood?

If they're interested in sexual activity with you, probably not.
If they're not interested, they'll be happier you asked them than if you 'just did it.' For example, they would prefer you initiate by asking to kiss as opposed to initiating by leaning over and kissing them. This is because they actually don't want to kiss you. And, that's ok. You only want to kiss people that want to kiss you. You'll find someone who does want to kiss you. It's good to know if

someone isn't into you, so you don't waste your time pursuing sexual activity with them and so you can respect them: their agency and choice of who can touch them.

Usually when people are into each other, they desire and feel turned on by having their romantic interest ask for permission to do sex acts and share what they want. Asks for consent are that. Discussing the sex that you'll do together is hot. I like hearing my crush ask, "can I kiss you?"

If anyone gets annoyed or offended when you ask for consent, then you probably don't want to have sex with them anyway or right away. Because, while you are trying to be clear about what is going on– what's ok and any boundaries or risks – which is morally right, they are either too immature to say what they want / to talk about sex, or they are trying to hide stuff.

In that scenario, you could be curious and ask them about why they seem irritated, annoyed, or some other emotion.

"I asked for consent and you scoffed. I imagine you are annoyed? Why is that?"

Are they uncomfortable talking about what they want or discussing sex? Why? Do they have something (an STI, relationship, past sexual trauma, body shame, sexual orientation / desire shame, etc.) they were hoping to hide and are now getting defensive? By being curious, asking, and listening to them instead of shutting down or getting angry/annoyed with them – you are opening up the opportunity for both of you to share and learn about each other and your unique sexual relationship.

Consent: It takes two "yes's" to start sex, but only one "no" to end it.

What isn't consent: any touch or sex act without permission first, needed for each instance and person. Also, agreeing to wear a condom / take birth control, then not doing it. Taking the condom off before sex while your partner can't see that and thinks you are wearing one is called **stealthing.** It's unethical, dangerous, and non-consensual.

Chapter 3. Question 2: "Do you have any STIs that you know of?"

You both want to know:

"Do you (my partner) have any **STIs** / sexually transmitted infections?"

"How do you know?" "When was the last time you got tested?" (It takes a few weeks to three months for some STIs to show up, depending on the STI and medical laboratory test.)

"When was the last time you had sex?" "Did you use **protection**?"

A sample flow chart of the **STI conversation**.

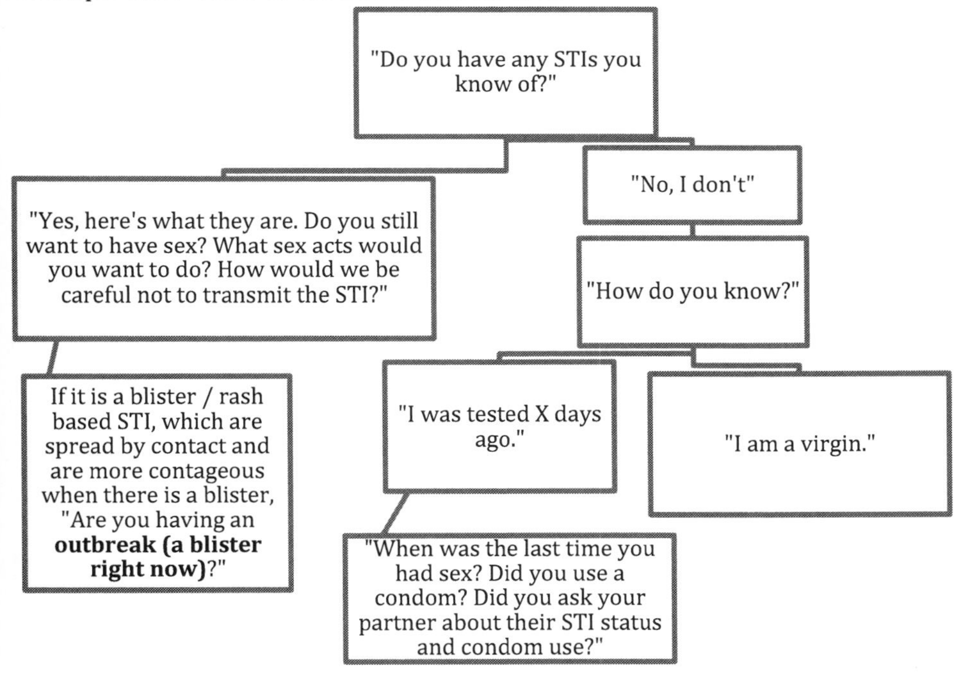

STIs, also known as sexually transmitted diseases or STDs, often have no symptoms and can be spread without symptoms. Some STIs are spread by touch and others by fluid transfer. Some are curable and others not. The surest way to know if you have one is to get tested, which you can do at a doctor's office or free clinic.

How to prevent STIs from spreading?

Safe sex is sex where you are careful to not spread STIs. It includes:

1) Talking to your partner about STI status, testing, and sexual history.
2) Getting tested regularly while you are sexually active. If you get a positive STI test result (which means you have an STI), telling your recent past, current, and future partners. Then getting treatment.
3) Using a barrier. A **dental dam** is a piece of latex that you can place over a vulva or asshole before kissing it. A **condom** is a barrier for a penis. A medical glove is something you can wear while touching someone's genitals, although unbroken skin is usually a good barrier.
4) Getting shots for STIs that can be prevented with vaccines (Hepatitis A and B, HPV) and/or taking medicine before sex to reduce the likelihood of transmission (for example, taking PrEP – pre-exposure prophylactics to prevent HIV transmission).
5) Having a **safe sex plan**: deciding ahead of time how you will proceed based on your partner's answers to the flowchart above. Maybe only having unprotected sex with a new partner after you both have been tested, if you both don't have STIs, or have been tested in the past 3 months after sex with another partner.

STI risks and prevention methods for each sex act:

Hand holding and hugging: risks are contagious skin rashes.

- If you see sores, blisters, or rashes, don't touch those.

Kissing: Herpes, HPV (contact spread STIs)

- If you see a sore / blister on their mouth / lips, don't kiss. STIs can spread even if you don't see a sore or blister: though it is less likely.
- Get HPV vaccines.

Touching and fingering genitals: Low chance for all STIs.

- Generally, your unbroken skin is a good barrier to prevent STIs.
- If you see a sore / blister / rash, don't touch it.
- If someone or yourself has an STI, touching it then a face, eyes, mouth, or genitals (or other mucous membranes) can spread that STI.

Oral sex (kissing genitals): Herpes, HPV, syphilis, gonorrhea, chlamydia. If the mouth has a cut: HIV, hepatitis.

- If you see a sore, blister, or colored mucus, don't kiss it or let it kiss you. Sores can exist in the area around genitals: inside of legs, above genitals, any spot covered by a bikini or underwear.
- If you don't see a sore, use a condom or dental dam.

Vaginal sex: All STIs.

- Use a condom and lube. (Use silicone or water-based lube.) The contact spread STIs, like herpes, syphilis, or HPV – ones spread by touch, can still be spread even if you are using condoms because the condom doesn't cover all of the genital areas.

Anal sex: All STIs.

- Use a condom and lube. That may not prevent the spread of all STIs as described above in with Vaginal Sex.

More resources: https://www.cdc.gov/STI.

Will asking about STI status ruin the mood?

No. If you have consent and are about to do some sex act, you both want to know if your partner has an STI, if they have been tested recently, when they last had sex, did they use protection, when was that partner last tested...

You want to know how risky it will be to have sex with them. Even if you use a condom, condoms break and contact spread STIs can still spread with a condom on. In my experience, asking about STIs has never ruined the mood.

If you have an STI, you tell your partner before sexual activity – even if they don't ask.

If you have consent but when you ask about STIs, your partner gets mad, you probably want to figure out why they got mad and/or not have sex with them.

Chapter 4. Question 3: "What happens if I or you get pregnant?"

After you have agreed to some sex acts, talked about STIs, and if one of you has a penis and the other has a vagina and you are putting the penis in the vagina or rubbing them together: you are at risk for pregnancy. If these apply to you, talk to your partner about pregnancy, pregnancy prevention, and what happens if that prevention fails.

Babies are made from a penis ejaculating into a vagina or through a medical procedure

Just like with STIs, you both want to know their thoughts. Here's what to ask:

1) "Are you trying to get pregnant?"
2) "If not, what kind of birth control are you / we using?"
3) "If that fails, what would you do?"

Various responses (not limited to this):

1) "I am not looking to get pregnant right now, maybe in a few years."
2) "Let's use condoms as birth control and STI prevention."
3) "If the condom breaks, let's split the cost of Plan B."

Your options if the birth control fails are:

1. Emergency contraception: Plan B or a copper IUD (if you take it within 72 hours after sex or place within five (5) days, respectively).
2. Get an abortion (length of access depends on your local laws and financial resources).
3. Keep the baby (raise it together or separately).
4. Give the baby up for adoption.

Ideally, you would agree to one of those options. If you **don't** agree:

- Don't have vaginal sex.
- Do other things: kiss, touch, spoon, oral sex, and anal sex.

- Use multiple types of birth control at the same time. For example, use a condom, 'pull out,' and take the pill – do all three of those.

Birth control is the phrase for pregnancy prevention. Humans have over 20 different types. See https://www.bedsider.org/ for more info. Note: if you are overweight, some birth controls including Plan B aren't as effective.

Will talking about pregnancy plans and what happens if the birth control fails ruin the mood?

No. You both want to know what the other's plan is if you / she gets pregnant. It's less stressful if you talk about it:

when there is no pregnancy risk (before you have vaginal sex) vs.

when there is a chance you could have a pregnancy (after you have vaginal sex) vs.

when you are sure you have an unplanned pregnancy (after a **pregnancy test**).

What if you don't talk about it? There's a good chance you will wonder if you / your partner got pregnant. A **pregnancy scare** is when you think you or they might be pregnant, and you don't want a baby. Pregnancy scares can be one of the most stressful experiences related to sex. I have, unfortunately, had my own share of pregnancy scares, and they are not fun.

My pregnancy scares... Here is a list of my pregnancy scares to illustrate the various ways this can happen (note: pregnancy scares are not limited to this):

1) During doggie style (sex from behind), I was having sex with a condom on. I came / ejaculated inside her and also inside the condom. That should have been fine because the condom should have collected all of the pre-cum and semen. However, when I pulled out, the condom was broken. All that was left was the ring of latex around my cock. Neither of us realized until I pulled out. (A way to reduce the likelihood that a condom breaks is to use it correctly – discussed more in Chapter 16 – how to use a condom. Essentially, check the date on the package and

that it has an air bubble. Squeeze the tip of the condom before rolling it down. Make sure you are rolling it down with the roll on the outside of the condom. If you get it wrong after touching it to the penis, get a new condom.)

2) I rubbed my penis against her vulva. I've done this more than once with different people. One partner and I called this, **The Dangerous Game.** It was dangerous because there is a chance they could have gotten pregnant from the pre-cum.

3) I used 'pull out' as a method of contraception. While that reduces the risk as opposed to me orgasming inside her, it was still possible she could have gotten pregnant. I don't recommend relying on 'pull out.'

4) We used a hormonal birth control that had sat out in a hot car in the sun during the summer. Lots of medicine can get changed (or ruined) by heat. Condoms may denature if left in a hot car. The ring, which according to my understanding releases its hormones based on heat when it is inserted in a vagina, if left in a hot car, may not be good anymore because it may have released the hormones in the car instead of the vagina. On the Nuvaring website, it says "Do not store NuvaRing above 86°F (30°C)." (Accessed December 10, 2019).

5) The girl didn't take the pill consistently. According to my understanding, for the pill to work properly, you need to take it at the same time every day. If you miss the times and worse if you skip days, the pill is a lot less effective. She missed days and didn't take it always at the same time every day.

6) We had unprotected anal sex. I came in her ass. I was worried the semen came out of her ass and then went into her vagina. Unlikely, but enough to cause both of us stress. Related was she wanted to keep the child if she accidentally got pregnant and I didn't. That made the scare much worse.

7) The condom broke, I had cum inside her, and she was overweight. Some emergency contraceptives, like the morning after pill, might be less or not effective for women over a certain weight. (Vogel, 2015) The copper IUD is an alternative effective emergency contraceptive.

Chapter 5. Question 4: "What type of relationship are you looking for?"

Before you initiate sexual activity, talk about your relationship goals and intentions.

Some people have sex to get into a relationship or expect sex would only happen in one. Others have sex for the temporary connection or want commitment-less sex. Some people get emotionally attached to whoever they just had sex with. Others, not so much.

Tell your partner your relationship intentions and goals. If you have different relationship intentions, don't have sex. If you don't want the same things, you probably don't want to have sex.

If you have relationship intentions that are different than your partner's, you are setting yourself up for emotional hurt.

How to ask about relationship intentions:

Method 1: Ask directly.

> "What type of relationship are you looking for?"
>
> "Do you see us as hooking up, friends with benefits, or is the first time of sex in a potentially long-term relationship?"
>
> "If we have sex, what does that mean for our relationship?
>
> "What other relationships are you in right now?"
>
> "When was your last relationship?"

Method 2: Tell them what you are looking for. See if they are ok with that.

> "I am not looking for a relationship right now. I am still attracted to you and would like to have sex with you. How do you feel about that?"

"I know I only want to have sex within a relationship. I want to make out with you and be in a relationship with you. How does that sound?"

Potential responses

- "I don't know (if I want to date (you yet.))"
- "I don't want to date."
- "I am only looking for hook-ups/dating/waiting to have sex until after marriage."
- "I am looking for a relationship with the right person."

Only have sex if you agree/accept each other's relationship intentions.

Story 4 Don't ask about relationship intentions *during sex*

I had a girl pause while giving me head to tell me she only wanted to continue if we were going to be in a relationship. I immediately said,

"Yes - of course. We are in a relationship."

But I wasn't sure if I wanted that with her. We had barely hung out.

After spending more time with her, I realized I didn't want to date. I ended our relationship, and she was upset. I imagine she would have been less upset if I was honest from the start.

Point of story: Talk about relationship goals before you're engaged in sexual activity because once you start, your partner may only be focused on sexual pleasure, even if you want to clarify relationship intentions during sex.

Will asking about relationship plans ruin the mood?

No. You both usually want to know the type of relationship intentions your partner has. Even if you only want sex and aren't looking for a relationship, you may want to only have sex with people that are ok with that.

If you really want a relationship, telling people what you want (and not demanding it of any one person) is the best way to get it (to ensure intentions are clear and potentially getting your desires met). To see if someone is into that, ask them. If they don't know, you can decide if you still want to fuck them.

Chapter 6. Preparing for Sex

I recommend prepping before you engage in sexual activity.

Understanding Agency

Agency means you control what happens to your body. And, other people control what happens to their body. You can always stop sexual activity (or physical contact) at any time. If you want to start sexual activity with another person, let them know, but know they have to say "yes" before you can start it with them because they have agency also. It takes two "yes's" to start but only one "no" to stop.

Body Prep

If you show up to a date smelling bad, you may not get laid.

Physical prep includes showering using soap under your arms, around your genitals and ass, wearing clean clothes, and using a breath mint or mouthwash. Some people like to shave – that's your choice.

Fingernails: if you might insert your fingers into someone's genitals, you could cut them with long, sharp, or jagged nails. Trim them, ideally a day in advance so they have time to become dull.

Cherry #2, Page 4.

Mouthwash

Bad breath is a turnoff. Mouthwash is better than brushing teeth because brushing can cut your gums, which creates entry points for STIs. Use mouthwash as an alternative.

Mind Prep

Think about what you want to do and how you will be safe

> What sex acts do you want to do?
>
> What do you not want to do? What are your boundaries?
>
> How do you want to prevent STIs?
>
> Do you want to always use condoms during vaginal sex?
>
> What pregnancy prevention methods are you comfortable with?
>
> Do you want to be in a relationship right now? If so, what kind of partner are you looking for?

You could make agreements with yourself. A best practice agreement is vaginal or anal sex should always be with a condom and lube that is safe for condoms –unless you both have been tested and aren't having unprotected sex with others.

Also, if you have shame about your body or having sex (because of religion, society, you're cheating on another person…), that may reduce your ability to get aroused, an erection, enjoy the sex, or have an orgasm.

Remember that sex is more than just visual. It is **all of your senses.** Their voice and moans. The taste of their lips and skin. The smell of their / your body, hair, genitals, and fluids. The feel of their body to touch. The warmth, wetness, soft skin, and firm erections. The pressure or light touch on your breasts. The feel of your genitals during penetration.

Wearing clothes that you like, that you feel sexy, cool, happy, or powerful can boost your confidence.

Cherry #2, Page 42.

Chapter 7. Boobs

Boobs come in all shapes, sizes, feels, etc. They are usually different sizes on the same person.

Lumps in the boobs are normal, except when...

People may like their boobs touched, kissed, or sucked. But, they only want this when they want it. To figure out if they want it, ask,

"Can I {insert your own verb} your boobs?"

They can also ask or tell you what they want,

"I like my boobs sucked on."

Some people like rougher play with their boobs: slapped, squeezed hard, nipples pinched, etc. To get this, ask for what you want and only do it if your partner wants to as well.

Chapter 8. Vulva / Vagina

A week of dry, a week of clear, a week of white, a week of red.
- a friend from a meetup describing the cycles of the vagina.

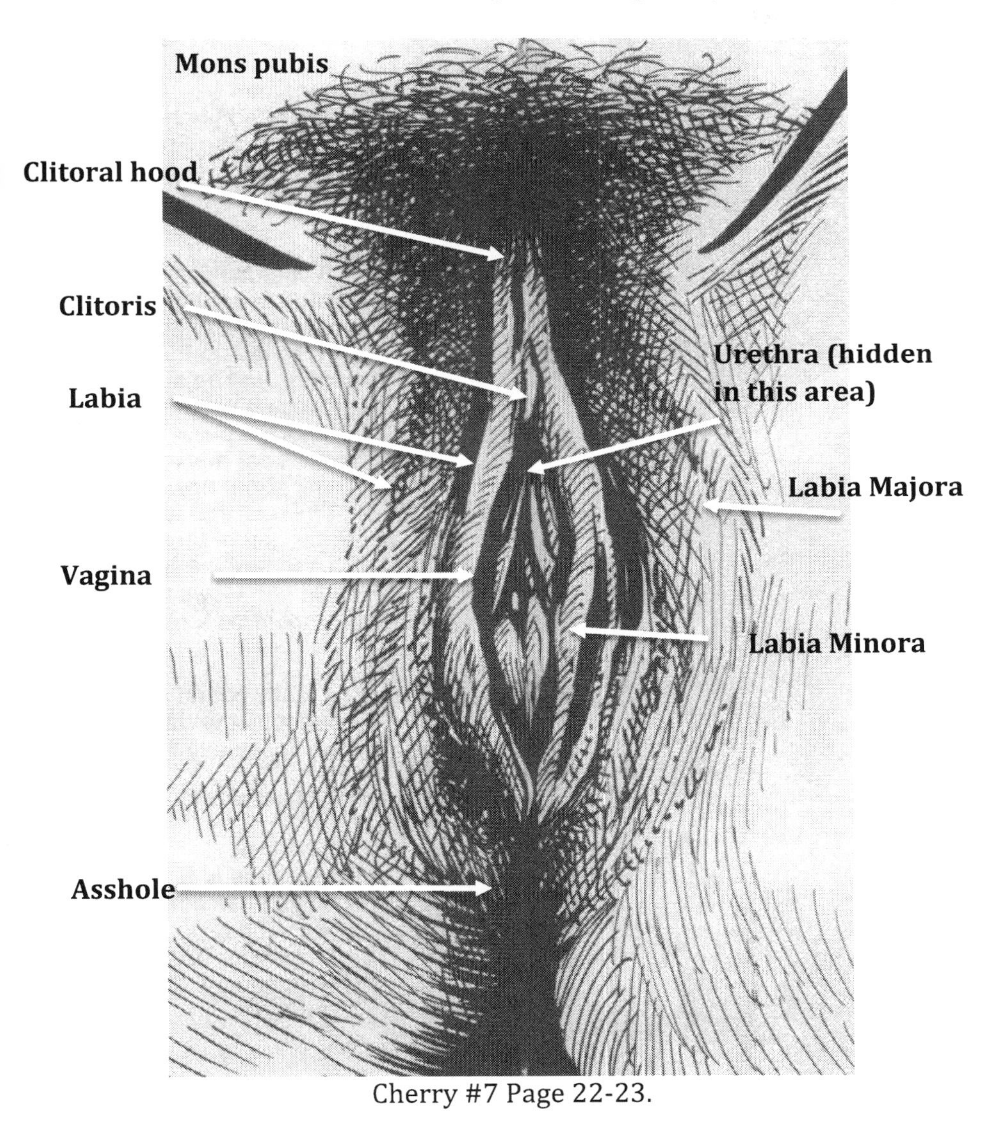

Cherry #7 Page 22-23.

Starting at the top is the **mons pubis**. This is a fatty part of skin that covers the pubic bone. This is usually covered in pubic hair or pubes. Pressing on this during sex or fingering can increase the likelihood of orgasm.

Below the mons pubis is the **vulva.** It is all of the visible genitals (in order from top to bottom): labia / lips which extend down the sides, clitoris and clitoral hood, urethra, and vaginal opening. People often call the vulva the vagina. The **vagina** or vaginal canal is technically a tube where things can go in and out, usually the penis during sex and babies during birth. The vaginal canal widens during sex and birth. During birth, it widens much more, and the widening is often a painful process. The inside of the vagina feels warm, wet, and squishy.

Vaginas have tiny glands that can produce clear or white liquid when a woman becomes aroused that lubricates sex. The liquid is called **vaginal fluid**. It is for reducing friction inside of the vaginal canal and on the vagina.

If a vagina or clitoris is stimulated to orgasm, it can **squirt**, which means to shoot out vaginal fluid. This is also known as **female ejaculation**. If you have a vagina, you may feel like you have to pee during sex. This is normal and may be the precursor to ejaculation.

Vaginas also bleed from the vaginal opening about once a month. That is called **the period**. The amount can change by month and by person.

Vaginas can also expel air from the vaginal opening. This is called a **queef** aka a vaginal fart. It happens when air gets caught then expelled from the vagina. It sounds like a butt fart but isn't smelly. Queefs happen during sex and a normal part of it.

Vulvas have two sets of lips: inner and outer **labia**. The outer, labia majora, looks like skin. It grows hair, and it feels fatty to touch. The inner can look like pink skin – similar to the inside of your mouth or it can other skin / brown colors. It is mucous membrane folds of skin. You can spread these lips open and run fingers, a penis, or things in and around them. This usually helps turn on a girl during foreplay.

Near the top of the vagina, below the mons pubis and under some folds of skin (the clitoral hood) is the **clitoris.** It feels like a squishy pea, bean, or peanut under the skin. The clitoris is often sensitive and a pleasure center. Touching the clitoris or near the clitoris in a repetitive motion is a way to help a woman reach orgasm.

How it works – touching or licking a clitoris: The clitoris is stimulated by soft touch and repetitive motion. Touch lightly, move slowly, move quickly, then back to slow. Move in circles, figure eights, or trace the cursive alphabet over it.

As the clitoris is stimulated, a woman feels sexual energy or tension build in her body. When the clitoris is stimulated enough, the woman feels a release of tension throughout the clitoris, vagina, and body. That is a clitoral orgasm.

Sometimes a vagina smells bad: it probably needs to be washed on the outside. Vaginas never need liquids to go inside to wash them. For women, all they have to do is wash with water. Their vaginas naturally clean themselves. Using any scented/abrasive soaps/wipes or douching can really mess up the pH balance of the vagina and lead to yeast infections or other problems.

You never need to put anything at all inside the vagina to clean it. Discharge is normal and will change in color/consistency/odor according to hormonal changes in a cycle. There can also be transitory changes in odor after intercourse because of the change in pH caused by sex/semen.

You should go see a doctor if the bad smells last more than a few days, itches/burns, and discharge changes in color/amount/consistency. Those are likely signs of infection.

Chapter 9. Penis and Balls

Penises come in various shapes, colors, sizes, and tastes. At the tip, they have a hole, which is the end of the urethra, which is a tube for pee and **ejaculate (or cum)**. The head of the penis is more sensitive than the shaft.

Some men have skin that covers that head of the penis (called **uncircumcised**). Other men had that skin removed, often at birth as part of religious practice.

How it works - arousal:

The penis is normally soft. When the owner of the penis gets aroused, the penis will get **erect**. The penis is known for getting **erections**, which means it goes from being soft and small to hard and large. When the owner of the penis isn't aroused, the penis is usually soft. A penis usually gets erect during sexual arousal, during stimulation, sometimes with a full bladder, and sometimes in the morning. Waking up with an erection is called **morning wood**.

After getting erect but before ejaculating, penises produce **pre-cum**. That is a slimy, milky-color fluid, comes out of this hole during arousal. If a man has yellow or colored mucous coming out of his penis, he has an infection and needs to go see a doctor.

Ejaculation often happens during the male orgasm. The ejaculate (noun) is a cloudy white slimy fluid (also known as semen that contains sperm.) It is used to make babies. When men ejaculate (verb) into a woman's vagina, the sperm mix with the egg (called fertilization). That makes a baby.

In addition to getting erections while sleeping, men can also ejaculate in the middle of the night while sleeping. This is known as **nocturnal emissions** or a **wet dream**.

How it works - touching or kissing a penis:

The penis is the pleasure center for man. Just like women, repetitive strokes, soft touches to the head, firmer grips on the shaft, general physical attention to the area increases blood flow and arousal.

Each man likes to be stroked differently so feel free to ask what feels good as you are touching it. Some similarities exist: A firm grip, using lotion/spit/lubricant, and using both hands. You can also use twisting motions and work your hands in motion together.

As a penis is stimulated, a man feels tension or sexual energy build in his body. When the penis is stimulated enough, it **ejaculates**. Ejaculation is the expulsion of semen and sperm from the penis. This is the male orgasm.

If a penis gets stimulated but doesn't orgasm, a man will get **blue balls**. Blue balls is an expression that describes physical pain in the testicles (and sometimes disappointment) from getting close to, but not, orgasming. The balls don't usually get blue. A thing to keep in mind is, men enjoy arousal and stimulation, but getting erect and aroused without orgasm, can be painful.

The penis can go in a hand, mouth, vagina or anus. A penis can also go between boobs. Men normally need help putting their penis in things, especially when they are new to sex and in the dark.

How to find:

The balls are below the penis and usually clearly visible.

How it works: touching balls: Balls can be very sensitive. Some men like to be touched there while others do not. You can always ask if they like it or not.

Some men like uniformed pressure applied. To do this, you lightly cup the balls, placing your hand around them. Slowly, you tighten your grip. You go slowly because you could hurt the man be squeezing too hard. You want to ease into it.

Touching the balls is like touching boobs – you can increase arousal for either of you, but you're not going to bring someone to orgasm by doing it.

Chapter 10. Butthole

Putting things in butts can feel good for anyone, but only if the person wants it.

The anus as a circular set of muscles – called the sphincter. It is naturally tight and closed. Those muscles need to relax before inserting anything into could be pleasurable. Or else it will be painful to have things go in and out of it. Don't force things in the anus. It usually takes time and patience to relax. Touching other body parts and / or kissing my help your partner relax their anus.

Learn how to relax your butt can be improved with practice. It's also easier if you are turned-on.

The following helps the butthole relax.

- Put lube on your fingers.
- Slowly rub the outside of your butthole while rubbing your penis or clitoris. If you're with a partner, you can also kiss and touch in any way that feels good.
- Touch the finger at the asshole. Gently apply pressure.
- Let the butthole relax and allow the fingertip to go inside.
- Don't push anything into the anus. Let the anus push out or relax to allow in the thing.
- Start with thinner items and slowly increase the width. Like, the handle of a small toothbrush, to a finger, plug, penis, to a wider dildo.
- Plan to communicate during this time. Let your partner know when and how hard to push.
- You start shallow - near the butthole then increase the depth.
- If your finger is inside a guy, you might feel his prostate. The closer you are to orgasm, the firmer and bigger the prostate will feel, like a squishy walnut. For women, you might find that you can reach her g-spot. You can rub these while rubbing their genitals.

You can practice this on your own with your own anus.

Anal sex / play doesn't mean poop will come out, although that can happen. It depends on the person and the instance. It's not a big deal if it does.

Cherry #10 Page 15.

Section II: During Sex

Ask for what you want and only do what your partner consents to do. Respect yourself and listen to your partner.

Chapter 11. How to Start Sex

After you have asked all of the questions in the first section, you say,

> "Are you ready to start? Do you want to kiss?"

If they say, "yes," you lean in and kiss them.

Cherry # 21, page 21.

When you want to do another position, you ask first. Let's say you want to take off their shirt. You ask, "can I take off your shirt?" etc. (the same for each act).

That's called **active consent** – asking at each act.

You can also give/accept **blanket consent** – permission for a bunch of actions up front. Even with this one, I still recommend asking before anal and rough play. Example of blanket consent with check-in before slapping:

> "You can whatever you want. I will stop you if I don't want to do it."

> "Ok"… During sex, "Do you like to be choked or slapped?"

Chapter 12. 10 Ways to Do Sex Acts Well

1) Go slow.

At the start of sex (i.e. if you start with kissing, kiss slowly), and at the start of each sex act (once you start penetration, thrust slowly and shallowly initially… this goes double with anal penetration).

2) Notice your partner during sex.

Pay attention to how your partner responds to when it comes to touch. Different people don't like certain areas touched that previous partners may have enjoyed, so it's good to pay attention to what does and doesn't feel good to their current partner.

For example, some people like being touched all over their body.

That generally feels good to people. For example, while you are kissing, run your fingertips on their arms and back. Or, while you are snuggling, same act.

However, some people may not enjoy being touched on their face, arms, back, sides, etc. They may not say it, but grimace, wince, or pull away when you do it. If they do, you can (and should) ask them, "I noticed you look unhappy. What's up? Is everything ok?"

3) Talk.

I cover this in the next chapter

4) Think of your partner's point of view.

"Men are afraid women will laugh at them. Women are afraid men will kill them." - (edited for clarity) Margaret Atwood (Dickson, 1996)

Sex is especially vulnerable for the smaller or weaker person. They are putting themselves in a position where they could be easily injured.

Consider that when you ask them questions. Ask with and genuinely have a caring, curious tone.

Try to imagine what it's like being them and what is important to them. Then check-in and confirm that, "Do you want x, y, or z?" They probably want safety, honesty, patience, orgasms, connection, ecstasy, lose themselves, etc. It can also change per day and act.

An example of this is that your partner probably wants the opportunity to have an orgasm, but you can ask, "Would you like for me to help you achieve orgasm?" Also, if you know you will be sleepy after you cum, help your partner cum first.

5) **Realistic expectations.**

   a) Sex should be enjoyable. If it's not, then stop and talk about what's going on and why. Use your problem-solving skills to fix it.

   b) Everyone is different. Different strokes (literally) for different folks.

   c) Not everyone will want to do all the things you do and no one can meet all your needs. That's ok. If you are both into each other, you probably have some overlap in things you want to do.

   d) Sex is messy –fluids, sweaty bodies rubbing against each other. It's part of the fun. Or, for some people – part of the discomfort. If you don't like feeling sweaty or wet, you can try turning on a fan or having sex in the shower or in an open space (i.e. living room floor).

   e) Be patient during sex. It takes practice to orgasm with another person. It takes practice to be good at fingering, handjobs, oral sex, vaginal, anal, their various positions. It takes practice getting the penis in the vagina or anus. Getting a position to work may take maneuvering and multiple attempts.

6) **Participate with your actions.**

   a) Move your body and hands to turn yourself on/improve the sex. Most women do not orgasm from penetration alone. Having a woman touch her clit or use a vibrator during penetration is the best practice for her to orgasm during penetration (Bloom, 2018). Try to move your hips together or take turns thrusting. The act of sex takes practice and coordination.

   b) If you lie there like a log (still and not doing anything), you are likely not going to orgasm or enjoy the sex as much (and neither will they) as if you actively do stuff. This could be thrusting, moving your hands on their body or your body, pushing into them, pulling them towards you, holding them, or providing counter pressure.

7) **Know you have the power to stop sex or change positions at any time or point.**

   If you are unhappy or about to become unhappy with the sex, it is better for you and your partner if you tell them. Ideally, the sooner the better. It takes two "yes's" to start sex, but only one "no" to end it.

8) **Use lube or lotion.**

   Use them for massages, handjobs, fingering, titty fucking, naked rubbing genitals together, vaginal sex, and anal sex. Use water or silicone-based lube if you are using a condom. The lube should say safe for use with condoms.

9) **Masturbate**.

   This is something you can do before you have sex and, depending on the act, while you are having sex.

   The benefits include self-esteem, the joy of orgasms, and understanding your body.

During sex, you can touch your penis or clitoris and help get yourself off – to reach orgasm.

10) Listen to your partner. Notice them during sexual activity.

If they seem really into it, you are likely doing something they like. You can ask them after. If they seem in pain or unhappy, you can stop, and ask them about it. Maybe they're not enjoying the current act or position or they have something else on their mind?

Sometimes your partner is trying to help you reach orgasm, find your clitoris, get their penis inside of you, etc. and they are having trouble. You can help them out by guiding them with your hand or words. This is a kind thing to do.

Chapter 13. What to Talk About During Sex

You are allowed to talk during sex, and I recommended it. Talk about:

1. Ending or pausing sex (I cover this more in a chapter called, "How to End Sex.") You can end sex at any time.
2. Changing positions or transitioning between sex acts.
3. Calling out usual things.
4. Having more physically enjoyable sex.
5. Reaching orgasm.
6. Sharing boundaries and goals. Asking your partner what they want.
7. Talking diry.

Ending or pausing sex: (and listening to your partner for this)

At any point during sex, you or your partner can end it. Listen to them for this throughout your sexual encounter. As soon as one person requests to end the sex act, their partner(s) must comply. If not, they are now committing sexual assault or rape.

It might sound like:

"I am good now."

"Wow that was great!"

"I've had enough, now it's your turn!"

"I really enjoyed making love with you. Let's rest."

"I want to stop."

"Stop."

"Let's take a break."

"I am no longer in the mood."

Even if you don't plan to end it (until you have an orgasm), you need to be listening to your partner in case they want to end it. As soon as one person wants to stop, you have to stop.

Transitioning between sex acts and positions:

You will likely want to do different sex acts and positions. To do that, ask! Ask what position and actions your partner wants to do. Even if you usually do anal, they may not want it this time. You need permission for each sex act and position every time. Ask for each one.

Asking at every action is call active consent. Only do it if they want to as well. This is how to transition between sex acts and positions. "Do you want to do doggie?" "Can I take off your underwear?" "Can I give you a hug?"

Examples:

- You're kissing, ask before taking off someone's clothes. "Can I take your pants off?"
- You want to move from the couch to the bedroom. "Would you like to go to the bedroom?" Although the bedroom might mean sex to you, you still need to ask if they want sex.
- You want them to touch you: "Would you like to feel how wet I am?"
- You want to initiate vaginal sex. Ask, "Do you want to have sex? Can I put on a condom?" They say, "yes." As you're putting it on, you ask, "What positions would you like to do?" They say, "Let's start with me on top." Later, you want to switch, "How would you feel if we switch positions to me on top?" or "Can we do doggie?"
- If you want to try a new position, know it will take patience + talking.
    - Ask to do: "Can we try with you on your side and me behind you?"
    - If they say, "yes," you still have to maneuver and figure out how to get the genitals to fit and stay in while thrusting.
- Seeing if they want to try something new:

- "I'd like to choke you. How do you feel about that?" Not everyone is into choking, hair pulling, ass-slapping, etc. even if they consented to anything.

Calling out the unusual things.

Sex should be enjoyable. If it's not, call it out and talk about it.

Call out your insecurities – like body, religious, or sex act **shame**.

- "I feel unattractive and want to keep my shirt on."
- "I was raised in X religion and I feel **shame** about my body and I think sex is wrong. I want to get over that, but I am not there yet.

Sex shame is a serious thing that comes from communities that teach sex, sexuality, sexual bodies, masturbation, sexual desire, etc. is wrong and should be repressed. The lasting effects of this can hurt peoples' sex lives well into adulthood.

Call out when you've lost presence. "You said something and I started thinking about that. I lost track of what you were saying. I last heard _____. Can you repeat from there?" This also works during sex.

Noticing their body, your body, or your feelings without shame or judgment. Share your visual observations, physical sensations, emotional feelings, thoughts, or what is going on with you in the moment. That shows vulnerability, opening space for your partner to share theirs, and for you two to connect more (Orgasmic Meditation, 2016).

> "I notice your pubic hair." "I see the brown color on your penis." "I notice the shape of your breasts."

Why? The goal is to reduce body shame and increase self-acceptance.

If you notice they don't seem into it, check if the sex is still welcomed:

> "Are you still into this?"

For example, they are scrunching their face as if in pain. You can ask, "Are you in pain?" Ideally, they would tell you, but they try to suffer through because you seem to be enjoying it. Sometimes people aren't good at communicating their feelings and needs, so it can be helpful if you take the initiative and ask, especially if they seem to not be enjoying the sex.

More fun, laughter, and enjoyment.

- You're allowed to ask random stuff and joke during sex.
- "Remember that one time when..."
- "Did you see the Bengals game on Sunday? What was that play?" (Some people are not into joking during sex. If you are and they aren't, they may feel annoyed if you joke.)

'Calling out the unusual thing' means when someone does something different, you can presence or name it. You say, "oh, you just did X. That was different. What's going on?" This is a technique from improv comedy. You use this to figure out what is going in your partner's mind (Black Box Improv Classes, 2017). 'Calling out the unusual thing' can reduce tension and reveal intentions.

Story 5 Calling Out the Unusual Thing – It might be initiation.

My girlfriend was having a party. Her friend was in town. At the end of the party, the three of us were cleaning up. When I brought trash into the kitchen, I saw them both standing face to face, a few inches apart.

I thought that weird, but it was my first day meeting her friend. I didn't know how their relationship normally worked, so I left and went to the master bathroom.

When I came out, they were lying on the bed smiling at me. Her friend was showing me up her skirt. I was thinking, "This is unusual."

I joked, "Is this that threesome fantasy I've always had?" My girlfriend responded, "Yes." Then the three of us had sex.

Point of story: When someone does something different, call it out. Another instance, a friend was sitting closer than usual to me as we were talking and eating ice cream. I said, "Are you trying to come onto me?" She responded, "yes." Then I asked if she wanted to kiss. She said "yes," so I leaned in and we started kissing.

Having more physically enjoyable sex.

Talking is the way to check-in with your partner to see how they are doing and improve sex.

- "Does this feel good?" "Is this going well?" "How is the sex going?"
- If the sex is painful, stop and talk about it. "Ouch, ouch – you're on my hair" (Dobkin, 2005). "You're crushing me." "This feels weird. Can we change positions?"
- If the sex is annoying, you can talk about it: "Your hair is my face. Can you use a hair tie?"
- Ask your partner to show you how they like a sex act (Joannides, 2017-2018)
  - **"Can you kiss me the way you like to be kissed?"** (If the kiss is bad, a girl is less likely to have sex than a guy. (Hughes, 2007). So getting this right is important.)
  - "Can you guide my hand on your clitoris? Can you move it in the motion, pressure, and speed you like?"

Ask for what you want.

- "Can you move to the right?"
- "Go slower/softer."
- "I like being spanked."
- "I like my nipples kissed and sucked."

Helping your partner get off (have an orgasm).

- "Could you reach orgasm with what we are doing? Would you like to? How can I help?" "Should we keep doing this or do you want to switch to a position that might be better for an orgasm?"
- "Up, down, left, right, harder, softer, faster, slower?"
  - Asking the above questions can help you help your partner reach orgasm and/or enjoy the sex the most.
  - People generally want to be a good sex partner. They want to help you reach orgasm. The trick is, only you know what feels

good in your body. To help them help you, you need to tell them what works / is working.

- If you see something working in your partner (like they say, "oh – I am about to cum"), keep doing exactly the same movement or stroke. However, feel free to explore in the beginning of sex acts. Do keep the same stroke after you have warmed up and change if they ask.

Sharing boundaries and goals

Say what you do/don't want and hear their boundaries/goals as well, which can happen any time before, during, or after sex.

- "I don't want to do anal tonight."
- "I don't like nails deep into my skin..."

Communicate your wants and needs. Ask and listen for theirs. If you need to pause, move positions, ask a question, want to try something, etc., ask or share.

Active Listening: As part of respecting your partner, you release your assumptions of what they want and actually ask them what they want. Then you listen to what they said and repeat that back in your own words. That gives your partner the opportunity to correct anything that you may have misheard/misunderstood.

Discuss goals. Sometimes you want an orgasm and they want connection. You or your partner won't know unless you talk. You don't always have to have an orgasm, but sex is generally the main way to get sexual pleasure.

- Other goals of sex can be emotional connection or pleasure (independent of orgasm). Sex can be fun and that is a fine reason to do it. If one of you is super focused on getting (you or themselves) off, it can add a bunch of pressure that works against orgasming or enjoying the sex.
- Tell them what you like between or during sex actions. Tell them what feels good. Help them get you off.
- Expect talk during sex. You are allowed to talk during sex. You are allowed to pause any sex action and start talking.

Talking Dirty

By talking dirty, I mean saying 'naughty things,' often whispered into your partner's ear or shouted as loud as you can. Usually it is about how much you want your partner, or the sex acts you want to do to/with them. Examples:

- "I want to fuck you so hard."
- "I want to fill you cum." (meaning to ejaculate inside someone.)
- "I want to feel your cum drip out of me."
- "I want to sit on your face."

Your partner may be into this type of talk or not. It's more of a sex act than a way to logistically improve the sex. Ask them if they like dirty talk:

"Do you want me to talk dirty to you?"

Dirty talk could enhance the sex, or it might be a turn-off / distraction.

Won't talking kill the vibe?

It depends - usually not. In the first few weeks/months of having sex with a partner, talking helps you figure out what they want and how to do it. Most people want that and won't get mad if you ask:

- "What feels good?"
- "How does this feel?"
- "What position do you want to do?"

As relationships progress, people change and may want different things. Talking is the best way to ask for what you want and to figure out what your partner wants.

Chapter 14. 11 Ways to Do Sex Actions Bad

1) **Anything without consent.**

'Just going for it' – like leaning in for a kiss, grabbing their butt, boob, vagina, penis, etc. could be sexual assault because you don't have their permission.

If they withdraw consent during sex, not listening or pretending not to hear and continuing having sex with them is now rape or sexual assault.

Listening but not believing your partner.

2) **Anything with pressured consent.**

Pressured consent means when someone says "no" and the other person doesn't happily accept that. Examples include:

Sighing. Telling them they are being a tease.

Asking "why not?" with an argumentative tone.

Using 'wear them down' strategy. This is where you keep asking for or bringing up something even after the person said "no" in hopes that they will get tired of your asking and eventually give in.

Emotional pressure: telling them how much it will mean to you or how much you really want them to do some sex act.

3) **Anything without caring about your partner's pleasure / needs / wants.**

Sex should be pleasurable for both of you. If it's not, stop.

Story 6

Once while in a relationship, my partner came home drunk and started kissing me. She was much more forceful than normal. As she kissed, she pushed her face into mine. Her hands wandered around my body, like usual, but instead of a gentle dance, she grabbed with force. I could feel her nails dig into my skin – not in a sexy way. I am sometimes into rough play, but only if we've talked first and I've asked for it.

I was not having fun. I was blocking and stopping some of her advances. I imagined myself as a goalie over my own body.

I think the worst part was when I wasn't reciprocating – when I was actively stopping her moves, she kept at the same rough pace. She didn't notice me in this – she seemed to be only focused on her pleasure, not noticing my blocks.

I imagined she was just trying to get her needs met and wasn't thinking about me. I felt sad and disappointed because I previously only knew her as a caring, thoughtful person.

Point of story: Any of the things she did (pressure, nails, being rough) could be hot, but only with consent and talking first.

4) Anything forced.

Either doing things you don't want to do or pushing fingers/fists/penises/dildos into butts or vaginas.

Holding their head/them so they can't leave. If you do this, you are now forcing them to engage in sexual activity with you. This could be during a kiss, oral sex, etc.

5) Doing things too hard.

Spanking, grabbing, twisting, forceful thrusting, etc. can be fun, but you need to ramp up with each time.

You have to build up trust.

You have to build a definition of *'what is hard?'* Start softly and slowly, increase with permission. After doing it softer, ask, "harder or softer?"

Too rough/violent: Spanking, hitting, choking, and hair pulling can be hot, but only if you both agree to it. If you 'just go for it,' your partner could feel turned-off.

6) Doing things too fast (either speed or intimacy).

Too fast - speed: Fast thrusting can fun, but you both have to be into it. As you start increasing speed, ask if it's ok. You can ask before you start, "could we try a fast speed this time?"

Too fast - intimacy: Some people have a physical intimacy pace in their mind:

The first three dates, no kissing

Then kissing on the fourth date.

Touching on the fifth date.

Oral on the sixth date

Vaginal/anal sex on the seventh date.

Other people are down to do it all on the first time they meet someone. It depends on the person. The only way you will know is if you ask.

7) Too risky

STIs, pregnancy, relationship intentions, or sex positions.

A penis can break or bend, which is a medical emergency. This can happen if the person with the penis is on the bottom because the weight of their partner coming down can land awkwardly on the penis. My suggestion is to practice this position while going slowly and shallowly.

If you have risky / unprotected sex related to STIs or pregnancy, immediately after the sex (and for the next few weeks), you might feel nervous that you contracted an STD or worry you got (them) pregnant.

8) **Bad smells in bed.**

Clean or wash yourself before being around others. I've noticed:

- Smelly feet – wash your toes.
- Breath – use mouthwash or a breath mint (vs. brushing your teeth if you are with a partner whose sexual/STI history you are unaware of).
- Farts - excuse yourself to another room before farting.
- Poopy butts. – wipe your butt until it comes back clean or wash it.
- Body odor under your arms.

9) **Too much unlubricated friction.**

Use lube for genital touching or penetration. Use lotion or oils for body or boob rubs. Saliva or vaginal fluid can be good to lube up fingers for the gentle touching of the clitoris.

10) **Manipulative goals.**

If you are trying to use sex to control someone (like getting them to be in a relationship with you because they had sex with you), this won't work and you will feel bad afterwards.

11) **Laughing at or shaming your partner about anything, really: their body, looks, actions, wants, needs, etc.**

If you laugh at them, they won't want to have sex with you again.

It's okay and even normal to laugh/giggle during sex if you're laughing together and not laughing at your partner. Sex should be fun and it's okay to laugh if you both bump foreheads or try a position that ends up being too awkward. It helps lighten the mood.

An example is laughing at your partner for queefing. They can't control that, and likely won't like you laughing at them for it.

The Sex Actions

If life was a video game, here are some sex actions you can do. I ordered them based on how I generally do them; however, there is no rule that says you have to kiss before you touch.

This section of sex acts I intend as a quick reference guide. I do repeat some info, like getting consent and starting each sex act slowly.

Expectations
Consent: You have to ask and get permission before you touch, before each act, each time you do it (unless you have agreed to blanket consent). Remember, it takes two "yes's" to start, but only one "no" to end any sex act.

Privacy: Most sex acts should be done in private. Eye contact, hand holding, hugging, can be done in public. Grinding is acceptable at some dances / clubs.

Orgasms: orgasming is usually easier by yourself than with someone else. It will take longer (or not happen at all) if you are putting pressure on yourself or your partner to have an orgasm. To cum, you must relax and focus on your body and feelings in the moment. Touch your penis or clitoris during sex to help yourself reach orgasm.

Different strokes for different folks: people like different acts and strokes. But, who is into what might surprise you. Ask what your partner wants and for what you!

Eye Contact

Eye contact is when two people are looking directly into each other's eyes. It happens when you look at someone and they look directly at you.

Eye contact can be hot, seductive, convey interest, and turn people on. It's often done right before kissing, in relationships, after kissing, during some sex positions, and oral sex.

People sometimes use eye contact as a nonverbal signal of interest: if someone keeps your eye contact for a second or longer, they may be romantically interested in or attracted to you.

Story 7

I was sitting on a bench next to a girl I knew from dance. We were talking, joking, and having fun. As the night went on, our legs were touching. I asked if I could put my arm around her, she said "yes" and I did. After, she slightly leaned into me.

We kept chatting. I paused, allowed for silence, and looked at her. She matched my gaze. We were making eye contact. I asked,

"Would you like to kiss?"

She said yes. We kissed.

Point of story:

I combined nonverbals

- eye contact
- sitting next to each other where our bodies are touching
- physical contact again with my arm around her

with asking for consent. That is a good strategy to initiate sexual activity.

Hand Holding

Related is holding arms, walking together in some form of an embrace:

Cherry #5, Page 27.

Definition: grasping hands together with another person and holding on, usually for a longer than a few seconds to minutes.

In my opinion, hand holding is the greatest ratio of emotional intimacy to physical intimacy.

Related is arm holding or interlocking elbows.

Use: emotional connection and, some people initiate hand holding to show or test interest (the test is if their potential partner holds their hand or pulls away.)

How to get into it: I recommend asking or reaching out your hand where they can see it and letting them decide if they want to hold it.

Sometimes people use a strategy of "accidentally" bumping their hand into yours and seeing if you hold hands then. Other times they 'just go for it' and reach for your hand and then hold it. I don't recommend either of those because the first is unclear and the latter is a consent violation. Asking shows confidence and is clear. If your partner wants it, being asked can feel sexy!

How to hand hold well?

- This is definitely a matter of personal preference. I like a soft grip. One of my girlfriends liked a firm grip – where our hands couldn't just fall apart. When I wasn't doing that, she told me she wanted a harder grip. That's good she expressed her wants. I wouldn't have known otherwise. I squeezed harder.
- One of my girlfriends liked **alternating squeezing:** she would squeeze my hand then I would squeeze hers. Then she would squeeze back. We would repeat this a bit. With other girls, it was one squeeze each. In these patterns:

  Alternating squeezing patter: X – Y – X – Y – X ...

  One squeeze each patter: X – Y ___(hold)______ ...

- Where X and Y are you and your partner squeezing.
- Sometimes after dances or hugging, I've had girls squeeze my hand.

How to hold hands bad?

- If you don't let go when they let go or pull away.
- If they pull away and you tighten your grip.

STI risk	Contagious rashes like scabies or ringworm
STI Prevention	Avoid skin-to-skin contact with someone who has a rash, is bleeding, or has an open wound.

Hugging

Cherry #2 (Welz, 1982-2000).

Remember, about asking before touching, even when consoling someone.

Story 8 Some people don't like being touched

At a meetup, someone told a very vulnerable and emotional story – the topic for that session was fear. This guy feared losing connection with his daughter and falling back into bad habits. After his share, I asked if I could pat him on the back. He shook his head and said he doesn't like to be touched.

Point of story: Some people don't like to be touched or hugged. The best way you know asking vs. doing it and violating their space.

Hugs are good for physically expressing emotional connection.

Related is arm around someone.

How to get into it: Ask if you can have a hug or if they would like a hug.

Special initiation: Aside from asking, you can spread your arms out, which many people see as a nonverbal hug offering.

I like firm, snug hugs for a second or two. But the time length, pressure, arm position, etc. depends on the person. If you hug someone a bunch, you can ask them how they like their hugs.

Bad hugs are anything forced, too long, too hard, or side hugs. If you don't want to hug, just say, "no thank you."

How to hug well?
It depends on the person. Hugs have a few dimensions: pressure, time length of hug, arm position, and body/torso position. I like:

- Firm hugs, unless one of us has asked for a light hug.
- A second in time length.
- Our arms at a diagonal.
- Chest to chest, a hug where your chests are touching.

How to hug bad?

- Hugging after they let go or start to pull away.
- In my opinion, side hugs because they seem like a hug for people who don't want to hug.

STI risk	Contagious rashes like scabies or ringworm
STI Prevention	Avoid skin-to-skin contact with someone who has a rash, is bleeding, or has an open wound.
Pregnancy Risk	None.

Grinding

(Draw your own image of grinding here.)

Grinding is people dancing together with their bodies touching, often someone rubbing their butt or leg against their partner's crotch – if one is behind the other or facing each other, respectively.

People usually do this because it is hot and fun and sometimes flirty.

How to get into grinding (This is one way.):

1) Go to a dance or club where people grind dance.
2) Make eye contact with someone.
3) Dance close to them. If they reciprocate and dance close to you, that's a good sign they are interested. If they move away, that shows disinterest.
4) Ask if they want to grind dance?

How to do it well:

- Try to stay on beat, move your hips side to side to the beat.
- Keep your hands on their hips. If they "drop it to the floor" (a move where the little spoon does a squat), move your hands slightly to the sides to give them space.
- Have fun.

How to do it bad:

- Not allowing them to leave or pouting if they do.
- Too much pressure that you are pushing the person over
- Grinding off-beat. You are trying to dance together. Try to stay on beat. This takes practice.

STI risk None if wearing clothes.
Pregnancy risk None.

Cuddling, Spooning

Cuddling looks like this, but lying down:

Cherry #17, page 20.

Draw your own picture of two people spooning in bed, which looks like a hug from behind while lying down:

Spooning is lying down next to someone where you are both facing the same direction. Your bodies are touching. It looks like a hug from behind while lying down. It's a type of snuggling, which is any form relaxing or lying down while holding each other. You can actually have sex in this position.

People do this for emotional connection and often talk during it. This can happen before or after sex or not lead to any other sex act.

People can also have sex while spooning. It's my favorite position right now.

How to spoon well:

- Getting into a position that is comfortable for both of you. I like one arm under the neck and the other over their body. Ask to rotate or reposition when you need to.
- Sometimes you or they will get too hot while spooning. Alleviate this with fans, covers (more or less), or repositioning.

How to spoon bad: None (other than the chapter on ways to do sex acts bad)

Concerns / FAQ:
It's normal to get aroused during spooning including for a person with a penis to get erections during spooning – especially if they are the big spoon.

Arms can fall asleep if they are positioned poorly. You can fix this by repositioning

If you want to start having sex while spooning, ask first. Don't just pull down their underwear or slip it in.

STI risk	None, unless you're both naked, then skin rashes.
STI prevention	Potentially reduced risk if there is no outbreak.
Pregnancy risk	None.

Kissing

Cherry #14, page 11.

Kissing, licking, or sucking necks are all related:

Cherry #14, page 11.

Kiss: touching lips together.
French kissing is open mouth kissing, sometimes with tongue.
Making out is kissing for more than a few seconds.
Hickies are bruises / marks on the skin and happen after you kiss then **suck** on someone's skin, often the neck. Your partner may not want one, so ask before you do it.
Biting lips, necks, or ears can be hot. Biting shouldn't cause bleeding.

Kissing is the first major sex act for most people in their life and in a new relationship. Start slowly.

How to kiss well:
Ask the person to kiss you how they like to be kissed. Also try,

- A slower, lingering, more intimate kiss is better at the beginning.
- First kiss for a few seconds or until they break away. The touch and stay allows you both to notice the feeling of the kiss.
- Keep kissing by alternating touching lips and breaking away.
- Breath and taste. On average, both men and women rate breath and taste as very important to whether they decide to kiss or will continue to kiss someone. (Note: Person hygiene is important!) (Hughes, 2007)
- Kissing with tongue might be too intimate for a first kiss. It is also a matter of preference: how much tongue? How deep? Tongue on the lips, the sides their mouth, or in their mouth? The best approach is to start with a little and see how they respond: do they mirror your tongue movement? Do they increase / escalate the amount of tongue?
- Touching while kissing can greatly increase the experience. Make sure you ask before you touch. Then move your hands around their body.
- Try different types of kissing.

How to kiss bad:

- Too much pressure - like pushing your face into theirs.
- Bad breath.

STI risk	Herpes, HPV, syphilis
STI prevention	Potentially reduced risk if there is no outbreak
Pregnancy risk	None.

Undressing

Cherry #4, page 14.

Undressing is often part of sex. You can do it in front of your partner or with their help. Sometimes the tease then the reveal of undressing is a key part of the experience, which turns people on and preps them mentally for other sex acts. The pre-steps before the final sex act, often some type of penetration that leads to orgasm, is called **foreplay**.

Logistically, you generally take off your clothes before sex.

How to take off a bra?
Bras usually have hooks in the back and are held together by tension. So, feel the middle of the bra on their back. Pull the two sides towards each other, which unhooks the two sides of the bra. Grasp the fabric on either side of the clasp, squeeze together, and release.

It takes practice (like learning any new skill). Some bras don't have hooks or hook differently. I encourage you to ask your partner for help if you need it. If they want you under their bra, they'll help.

Ripping off underwear. Often undressing is a slow, sexy process. The opposite, a fast, violent act of tearing someone's clothes off their body can be hot. Ask before you do it. I generally ask, "do you like this pair of panties?" – as the surprise of tearing off can add to the hotness. If they say "no," I'll rip them off. If they ask "why?" I'll tell them my plan to rip them off.

STI risk	None.
Pregnancy risk	None.

Touching, Exploring, Caressing, Massaging Body Parts (any spot but genitals)

Cherry #6, page 4.

Touch is important during any sex act. When having sex, you often do more than one thing at a time. Like, you'll be having vaginal sex and be hugging and kissing. Like, while facing each other where one person is on their back on the other on-top, you can touch their body, kiss their chest or neck, bite their ear, or hug them. Or, you could be kissing and rubbing each other's arms and backs.

A friend of my likes, while spooning, having her partners run their fingertips up and down her arms and body. This exploring with fingers can really turn her on.

Touching genitals is covered later.

How to caress someone (non-genitals) well:

- Start softly. Pretend your fingers are feathers, lightly across their body.

- Take your time to explore.
- Often, if the person wants more pressure (wants you to squeeze their body), they can grab your hands and squeeze/push them onto your body. You can also ask (and talking during sex actions is great!). Ask,
    - "Harder/softer?"
    - "Faster/slower?"
    - "Up/down? Left/right?"
- You can tell them what's good or can be better. You can use nonverbal feedback by taking their hand and showing them what you like.
- Try running your hands through their hair while snuggling or kissing.

For massaging – use lots of lube and lotion. If you have both discussed and agreed to get naked, if both parties get all lotioned, oiled, or lubed up, that can be incredibly hot.

How to do it bad:
- Pinching, unless they say they like it.

STI risk	Skin rashes and infections
STI prevention	Avoid touching someone with a rash or open wound or wear a glove.
Pregnancy risk	None.

Rough Play

Slapping, spanking, hitting, choking, squeezing, holding down, scratching, hair pulling.

!!!!!!: Don't actually hurt them !!!!! The goal of these sex actions should be fun, hot sex actions. None of these should leave lasting marks, cause injury, or lead to death. Temporary marks can be ok. Always start softly for a short amount of time and slowly increase pressure.

How to do it:

Step 1) Ask if they want to try it.
Step 2) If they say "yes," ask, "How hard?"
Step 3) Do it softer than you think they asked.
Step 4) Ask them if they want another and if so, softer or harder.

Spanking (and any type of rough play including hitting, choking, holding down, bondage, etc.) requires additional talking: consent, limits, safe words, pressure amount preferences, etc.

Safe word is an agreed upon word that when said, you stop and check-in. The most common are "red" and "yellow." "Red" means "stop immediately." "Yellow" means "this is getting close to my boundary. Don't go any further"

Spanking: open hand hit their butt. Can be done over clothes or bare skin.

Hitting/slapping: open or closed hand on a body part.

Choking: restricting airway or breath with your hand or arm. Use extra care with choking. This one could kill or seriously injure them. That would definitely ruin the sex for both you. To avoid that:

- Do this with someone you trust.
- Do it only a short time. Pause and check-in.
- Start with low pressure.

- Hand positioning is also important to not injure them. Grip under the chin vs. near the Adam's apple. Apply pressure on the carotid artery.
- Use caution and watch their face. The person being choked should not pass out. If they pass out, stop doing this. Let them breathe normally.
- Research more on how to do this.

Squeezing: this is grabbing a body part and increasing pressure. Squeezing can hurt someone and leave marks for days. If you're squeezing testicles (covered more in the Ball Play chapter), make sure you squeeze directly towards the center vs. twisting. If you twist, you can cause serious injury.

Holding down: this is grabbing someone's body parts (like arm, wrist, shoulders, etc.) and keeping them in one position - often down against the mattress.

Scratching: this is running your fingernails against someone's skin - often their back. Depending on how hard you do this, it will likely leave marks (which are tiny cuts.). The marks should heal in a few days.

Hair pulling: run your fingers through their hair and move close to the scalp. Grab hair closest to their head instead of at the end / tip. Pull gently. You can do this from any position/act: i.e. from behind or during kissing.

Summary notes:

- Establish safe words or signals.
- Touching base / checking in / asking how it was after each action.
- Start with
    - Low pressure
    - Short time
    - Asking after each rough action how it was for them

STI risk	The red spots left after spanking are small cuts which could spread STIs.
STI prevention	Wash your hands after or wear gloves or use toys.
Pregnancy risk	None.

Masturbation

Cherry #3, page 4.

Masturbation is playing with yourself for sexual pleasure. It can be touching your genitals, penetrating them, or using toys/vibrators/objects to sexually pleasure yourself.

Masturbating can build self-confidence (because you directly improve your life by making you feel good), be relaxing, and reduce tension.

Masturbation is normal, healthy, and will help you enjoy sex more. Unfortunately, it has gotten a negative press in some religions, cultures, and time periods.

Girls usually rub their clitoris (the top of the vagina – the spot that feels pleasurable when rubbed) and insert fingers/things into their vagina. Girls can use a towel/shirt or a pillow/stuffed animal between their legs. Grab it with one end in front and one end behind. Then grind on it.

Boys usually tug on their penis, squeeze it, and pull up and down it. Boys can use their underwear to add pressure. Lying on one's back, pull the underwear down just below the butt. Then push the erect penis under the elastic band. Then, pull the penis above the front of the elastic band. That creates tension on the penis with the underwear. It can feel good.

Anal Masturbation - any gender can put clean things inside their asshole such as a toothbrush or hairbrush handle. If you do this, you want to use lubricant, which you can buy at a drugstore or grocery store.

How to do it well: Do whatever feels good or you want to explore.

How to do it bad: Hurting yourself. Avoid that by using lube and cleaning any sex toys. If you use warm water, make sure it isn't too warm (hot) before putting it on your genitals.

STI risk	Spreading an STI to another body spot.
STI prevention	Wash your hands before you touch your face, eyes, mouth.
Pregnancy risk	None.

Touching Breasts

Cherry #14, page 11.

Touching breasts is fun. Make sure you have permission before you do it.

How to feel someone up (touch a breast) well:

- Ask your partner. Do they like your touch? If so, do they just like gentle rubbing, pinching, do they need lubrication on the nipple first? Etc.
- Start softly – cupping or caressing. Pretend your fingers are feathers, - lightly draw circles or patterns across the nipples.
- Take your time to explore it, especially if it's your first time or anytime you want to.
- If you want someone to squeeze harder, ask.
- Nipple orgasms exist and can be achieved with strokes particular to each person (and sometimes with kissing breasts – covered later.)

How to do it bad?

- Pinching, unless they say they like it.

STI risk	Skin rashes.
STI prevention	Avoid touching if either of you have a rash on your hand or breast.
Pregnancy risk	None.

Touching a Vulva/Fingering a Vagina

Cherry #16, page 31.

Touching a vagina is an important sex act because it is a way to bring a woman to orgasm. This can be penetration with fingers and focused, light, repetitive touch on the clitoris. Doing this before vaginal or anal penetration can help a woman orgasm from penetration. Also, you can do this while penetrating.

How to do it well:

- **Prep**: Wash your hands immediately before. Trim your fingernails a few days before so they are short and dull.
- **Teasing** move towards her vagina and then away. Start touching the inner leg. Then loop around her stomach, sides, and lower legs. Once you do touch the vagina – touch all around it: up and down, inside the lips. Find the clit / clitoris and glance (lightly, barely touch it) across it. Go back to the rest of the vagina then come back to the clit.
- **How to find the clitoris: start at the vaginal opening and run your finger up towards her belly. It will feel like a pea under the skin.**
- After a few glances of the clit, **focus on the clit**.
- **Stay touching the clit**. Let her stop you when she is ready.
- **Start softly**. Too much pressure can hurt. The clit is very sensitive.
- The stroke: Gently rub up and down on the clit: towards her stomach then back down towards her vaginal opening. using a circular stroke.

- **Pick a stroke and stick with it**. At least for 90 seconds at a time. As opposed to switching back and forth between circular to zig / zag.
- Lube up using her vaginal juices or actual lube to lubricate the clitoris.
- If / when you penetrate the vagina, move slowly and shallowly in and out at first. Build up to deep, fast strokes.
- You should talk to her while you are doing it to see if you are doing it right. Ask: Harder, softer? Left, right? Up, down? Faster, slower?

How to do it bad:
- If she pushes your head to her vagina – trying to force you to kiss it.
- If it's too dry. Use lube to fix this.

STI risk	If an abrasion or cut on the hand: herpes, HPV, syphilis, HIV, and hepatitis.
STI prevention	Latex glove and lube.
Pregnancy risk	None.

Related – Fisting a Vagina

Fisting a vagina is an uncommon and advanced sex act. You can seriously injure her if you jam/force in the fist. To do it, slowly increase the number of fingers inside. If you are both into it, it can be fun.

Cherry #13, page 11.

Same risks as touching a vulva/fingering.

Touching a Penis

Cherry #16, page 31.

How to do it well: If you are touching his penis, you are already winning in his mind.

- Use a lubricant: lotion, lube, vaginal fluid (adds STI risks), spit. If the penis becomes dry or sticky, reapply. If you don't have lube, you can use lotion. Know that some lotions get sticky after multiple strokes so you may have to reapply.
- Try different grips. Use both hands. Stack your hands
- Some guys like ball play.
- Some guys like anal play – ask first.
- When he starts to cum, reduce your pressure. Touch the penis very lightly during orgasm.
- When a penis cums / orgasms, it ejaculates fluid in a series of short bursts.

For the person receiving the handjob:

- Tell your partner when you are about to cum. They may want to point the ejaculating penis in some specific direction (like on their chest).
- If you want to ejaculate on your partner, tell them and ask if they want that also. (If you want him to ejaculate on you, ask him to.)

Reaching an orgasm may take time. It will take longer (or not happen at all) if either of you are putting pressure on yourself to have an orgasm. To cum, you must relax and focus on your body and feelings. Try to enjoy it.

How can a handjob be bad?

- If the guy is trying to make you suck his penis. If he is **pushing your head** down to his penis, that is bad. Tell him not to do this or you'll leave. If he does it again, stop, get up, and leave.
- If the handjob is dry or becomes sticky. Penises can rub raw. Use lube
- You are using your fingernails. You could cut the skin and feel painful.
- You are twisting their balls - can be extremely painful and lead to a serious medical condition.

STI risk	Herpes, HPV, syphilis. If you have a cut on both body parts, HIV and hepatitis
STI prevention	Condom or latex glove, and lube.
Pregnancy risks	None.

Related – Ball Play

You can seriously injure the guy by twisting his balls. Squeezing into the ball (vs. twisting) is the way to go. Squeeze softly at first and then increase pressure. Squeeze directly into the center of the ball instead of twist.

Same risks as touching a penis.

Touching a penis can bring it to orgasm.

Touch Behind

Ass grabbing can be hot, but only if you have consent (as with any sex act). Don't just grab a butt. Grabbing a stranger's butt (or any genital, really touch anywhere) is inappropriate, offensive, immoral, and likely illegal. Don't do it. If you want to touch, grab, spank someone's butt, ask first.

> "Can I touch your butt?"

(It generally helps if you are in a setting where that might be appropriate: like at a fetish Halloween party, swinger's club, alone with your partner vs. a workplace or religious setting.)

How to do it well:

- Asking
- Gently squeezing initially.
- Asking if they want you to squeeze harder or softer.

How to do it bad:

- No consent
- Squeezing too hard initially. If your partner asks for harder, go ahead.

STI risk	Skin rashes.
STI prevention	Avoid touching if either of you have a rash on your hand or behind.
Pregnancy risk	None.

Related Acts: Spanking is hitting a butt and is covered previously in the rough play chapter. Start softly, slowly increase pressure, and communicate the entire time.

Finger(s) in anus (and fists)

Go slow and use lots of lube.

Some lubes, like thicker silicon-based lubes (instead of some water-based lubes), are designed specifically for anal play. They are thicker in consistency and some even have numbing effects for people worried about the pain.

Consent and notice is important here as people tend to get thrown by a finger in the butt without prior warning, even if they have agreed to the sex act.

Start so slow as to just play around the outside of the anus with a soft touch to check in and make sure the partner is feeling comfortable (unless asked otherwise).

How to do it well:

- Asking first is the best practice before trying to put a finger in a butt.
- Use a lubricant: lotion, lube, spit. If the anus becomes dry, reapply.
- The person putting in their finger needs to touch the butthole.
- Then, slowly and gently apply pressure. That gives them a chance to say no, pull away, or push your hand away.
- The finger has to be let in by the butthole so it can be pleasurable.
- Once inside, slowly move in and out as pleasurable.
- You can practice on your own anus.

How to do it bad:

- No consent
- Jamming or forcing fingers in the butt.

STI risk	If an abrasion or cut on the hand: herpes, HPV, syphilis, HIV, and hepatitis. Butt bacteria can be bad for the vagina.
STI prevention	Latex glove and lube.
Pregnancy risk	None.

Oral sex – hand, body, and feet.

Kissing, licking, sucking, etc. ears, necks, collar bones, sternums, stomachs, backs, arms, legs, feet, armpits ... can be hot and turn people on. With consent, it's good foreplay.

How to do it well:

- Ask or tell your partner what you like.
- Explore around with your mouth after you get consent.
- Some people really like their toes sucked and they don't even know it until it happens.

How to do it bad:

- Anything forced / without consent.
- Leaving hickies in visible spots if unwanted.

STI risk	Low risk of herpes, HPV, syphilis. If a cut on both the mouth and body part: HIV, hepatitis.
STI prevention	Put a dental dam over the area before you kiss it.
Pregnancy risk	None.

Oral Sex – Breast

Cherry #1, page 24.

Kissing, licking, sucking breasts and nipples.

How to do it well: Kiss and suck. Try different things. Ask your partner to kiss you how they like to be kissed.

I've had a partner that loved her nipples being sucked. Another could orgasm from that.

How to do it bad: anything without consent.

- Biting too hard initially. Bite harder if they ask

STI risk	Herpes, HPV, syphilis. If a cut on both the mouth and body part: HIV, hepatitis.
STI prevention	Dental dam
Pregnancy risk	None.

Oral Sex – Vagina

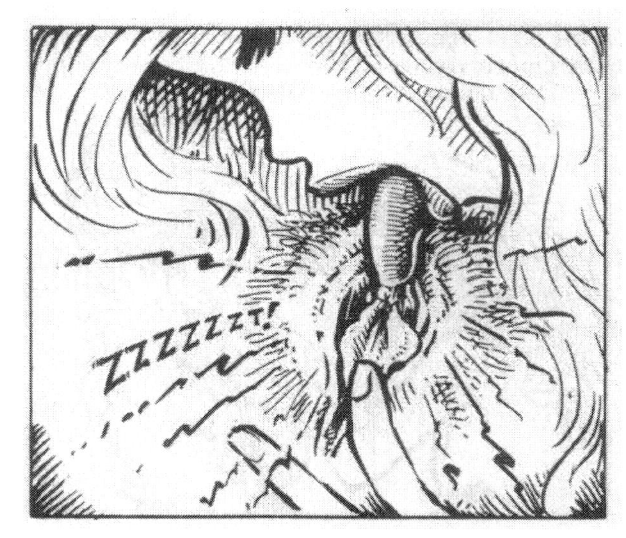

Cherry #18, page 9.

Kissing, licking, sucking all parts in and around a vulva.

Focus on the clitoris, as seen above, to help her reach orgasm.

How to do it well:

Initiation:

1. Start with kissing.
2. Continue with touching your hands over their body. Touch over the clothes over their vagina.
3. Continue with undressing them.
4. Kiss down from their mouth, to their neck, chest, stomach, and waist. If at any point they stop you, stop.
5. Most women initially like teasing. Draw concentric circles kissing getting closer to the vagina each time.

While continuing kissing the vagina:

- Exploring the entire vagina increases arousal.

To reach orgasm:

- Repetitive motions on the clitoris lead to orgasms.

- Consistent tempo or rhythm.
- Try different speeds. Usually a fast speed at the same tempo achieves orgasm.
- Try different strokes:
  - Up and down
  - Circles
  - Figure eights
- Try different pressures.
- Spend most time at the clitoris. Do most of your stroking on the clitoris.
- Use a mix of soft/firm pressure.
- Take breaks by using different positions or your fingers.
- Give and get feedback
  - Left right
  - Up down
  - Harder softer
  - Slower faster
- Get into it, enjoy it.

Not every time you will reach orgasm. If you expect it and it doesn't happen, you can get disappointed.

How to do it bad:

- No consent.
- Unclean or smelly vagina. Good hygiene is important.
- Oral sex on your period can be ok if your partner is ok with that.
- Using teeth.
- Pushing someone's head towards your crotch to have them kiss your vagina.

STI risk	Herpes, HPV, syphilis, gonorrhea, chlamydia. If a cut on both the mouth and body part: HIV, hepatitis.
STI prevention	Dental dam
Pregnancy risk	None.

!!! Brushing teeth before oral sex can cause cuts in the mouth (entry points for STIs) - use mouthwash as an alternative.

Oral Sex – Penis

Kissing, licking, sucking a penis or balls.

Cherry #9, page 7.

*Touching yourself while giving oral sex can enhance or distract.
*Let your partner know when you are about to cum in their mouth. They may not want it there.
*It's good to ask for what you want, "Ooo! Now I want it in my mouth!"

How to do it well:
As with most hand and oral sex actions:

- There is no one right answer. Do it how it is fun for you while respecting the other person.
- Repetitive motions lead to orgasms
- Go up and down
- Get into it, enjoy it
- Use a little suction
- Focus on the head (tip of the penis)
- Take breaks by using different positions or your hands.
- Use your spit as lube: spit out as you gather saliva in your mouth.

- Give and get feedback
- **Deepthroat** or deepthroating is putting the whole penis in a mouth. It is a type of blowjob. Often to do this, you have to suppress your gag reflex.
- If you are receiving the blowjob, you can hold their hair or lightly touch them. Or, you can keep your hands off them. Don't push their head down unless you talk to them about that.
- **Throat fucking** is a blowjob where the person with the penis is moving their hips back and forth while their partner's sucks their penis. Most blowjobs or the traditional blowjob, the person with the penis doesn't move their hips or only moves in and out lightly.
- **Tell your partner when you are going to come.**
    - When a penis cums, it ejaculates semen. It shoots that out in a series of short bursts. The partner may want that ejaculate in a certain place. The only way they can achieve that is if you let them know.

How to do it bad:

- No consent
- Using teeth
- Pushing their head into your body without consent
- Thrusting with force into their mouth without consent

STI risk	Herpes, HPV, syphilis, gonorrhea, chlamydia. If a cut on both the mouth and body part: HIV, hepatitis.
STI prevention	Condom
Pregnancy risk	None.

Oral sex – Anus

Kissing, licking, sucking an asshole or butt.

Most people do this for sexual pleasure.

How to do it well:
Most people can't orgasm from getting their ass licked, so most people don't try to make that happen.

- I don't know of any special technique, just do what feels good.
- Lick the butt hole.
- Put your tongue in it.
- Put your finger in it slowly.

How to do it bad:

- No consent

STI risk	Herpes, HPV, syphilis, gonorrhea, chlamydia. If a cut on both the mouth and body part: HIV, hepatitis.
STI prevention	Dental dam
Pregnancy risk	None.

Breast & Penis Contact

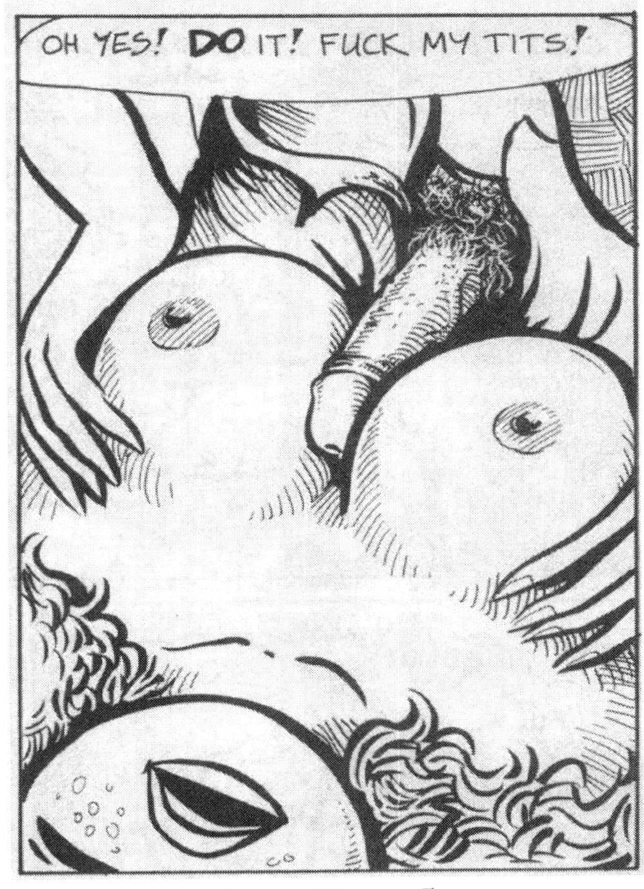

Cherry #7, page 5.

Breast-penis contact can be sexy. Squeeze the breasts around the penis. Use lube.

How to do it well: Use lube and communicate.

STI risk	Herpes, HPV, syphilis.
STI prevention	Dental dam or condom
Pregnancy risk	None.

Vulva & Penis Contact

Grinding the penis in-between the lips/labia of the vulva, rubbing the penis head against the clitoris, etc.

Use lube.

STI risk	All STIs.
STI prevention	Condom
Pregnancy risk	Almost non-existent: sperm exists in precum. Increased risk if the penis recently ejaculated.
Pregnancy Prevention	17 options, see bedsider.org.

Vulva & Vulva Contact

Scissoring.

Use lube.

STI risk	Herpes, hepatitis, HPV, and syphilis. If either of you have an open wound/sore: all STIs.
STI prevention	Dental dam
Pregnancy risk	None.

Penis & Penis Contact

Use lube.

STI risk	Herpes, hepatitis, HPV, and syphilis. If either of you have an open wound/sore: all STIs.
STI prevention	Condoms and lube.
Pregnancy risk	None.

Vaginal sex

Cherry #10, Page 10.

Vaginal sex is the way to get someone pregnant. When a man ejaculates in a woman. That is called a creampie. It looks like above.

Vaginal sex is penis penetrating the vagina. Slowly insert it and consider using lube. If anything is painful, stop. Some women have vaginismus, which makes it impossible for the penis (let alone a finger) enter the vagina, so don't try to force it.

Period sex, or sex while she is on her period, is cool as long as you both are cool with it.

If it is a woman's first time, she may or may not bleed.

At least one of you has to move their hips or body or else you will just be lying there with penis in vagina. Often, only one person is thrusting. I believe sex is better for both people if each person is thrusting, although this can take more practice... which may be a fun thing.

Longer sex is usually better. In many people's minds foreplay counts towards that time. So, you can increase the length by having more foreplay.

If the guy 'cums too fast' and lose their erection, relax because he can get another. You both can cuddle, chat, or give oral sex between erections.

Touching the clitoris can be a great way to help her orgasm during penetration. Men usually can cum from penetration alone.

Queefs are vaginal farts. They happen when air gets caught in the vagina and then expelled. Sometimes this can happen during vaginal penetration. If you laugh or shame her for queefing, she likely won't want to have sex with you again.

Just the tip is a play on words for a sex act of putting just the tip or head of the penis in something, usually a vagina. It is suggested because it may be less scandalous or as a way to lead to sex. Unless both people enthusiastically want to play 'just the tip,' don't do it. Don't pressure people into sex, even if it's just a little bit of penis / some sex act.

How to do it well:

- Washing your body before sex.
- Communicating what you want during sex.
- Going slow initially.
- Practicing.
- Using lube.

How to do it bad:

- Anything forced or without consent.
- Not communicating your needs.
- Not noticing your partner and asking if they are "ok?"

STI risk	All STIs.
STI prevention	Condoms or female condoms and lube
Pregnancy risk	Yes. This is the sex act to make babies.
Pregnancy Prevention	17 options, see bedsider.org.

Anal sex

Cherry #12 Page 10

Put a penis in an anus. Go slowly and use lube.

How to do it well:

- Go slowly and use lube.
- Use lube. I like silicone-based lube, especially with condoms.
- Let the anus relax and allow the penis in as opposed to pushing it in.

How to do it bad:

- No consent.
- Pushing things into the anus.
- No lube.
- Going from ass to vagina – because the butt bacteria is bad for the vagina.

STI risk	All STIs.
STI prevention	Condom and lube
Pregnancy risk	None.

Sex Positions

Sex gets better with practice. So does each position. Expect to take time to figure out how to get them to work/fit your parts together. Here are a few to consider:

On top / cowgirl
This great for sucking breasts.

Cherry #4 Page 7.

On top / cowgirl. Cherry #8 Page 26.

On stomach/pronebone

- This position can be done anally or vaginally.
- I suggest having your partner's legs straight and together, and then spread their cheeks."

On back / missionary

- Many people enjoy eye contact on entry and throughout sex. You can easily do it with this one and on top.

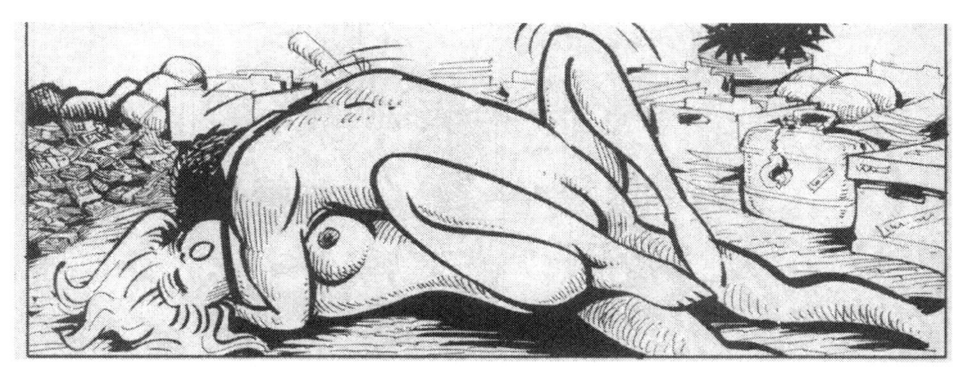

Cherry #5 Page 3.

From behind / doggie / on knees

Cherry #4 Page 8.

Spooning

While many people may want to spread their legs open to get into this or bend away (like you are doing doggie lying down), I like their legs straight and together.

****Spooning** is one of my favorite positions. It looks like doggie style, but both of you are lying on your side. It is great for vaginal sex and even better for anal sex.*****

Facing spoons – another sex position where you are lying on your sides, facing each other, and having sex.

Standing

- One standing, one on some furniture. (Be aware of height differences when finding a position that works)

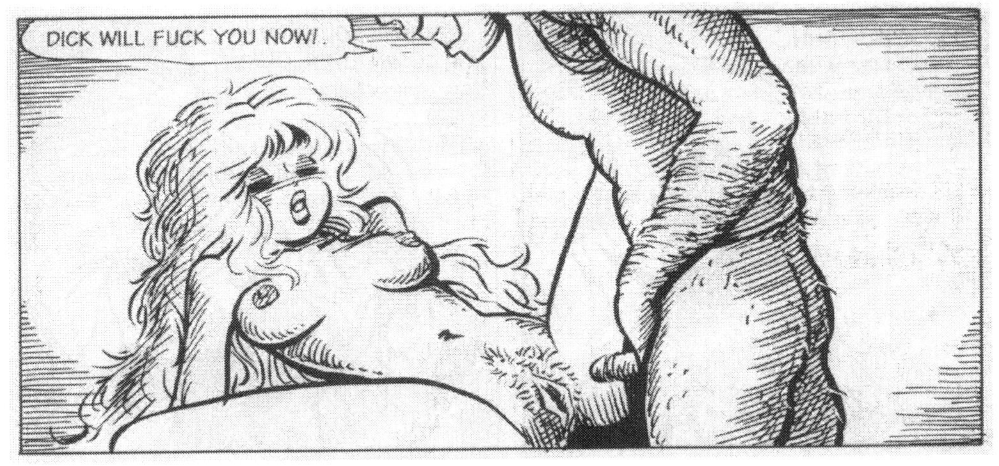

Cherry #19 Page 5.

Chapter 15. How to End Sex

In my experience, sex usually ends organically after both partners have orgasmed, although that usually happens at different times. However, this isn't always the case, and sometimes someone wants to end it sooner.

You or your partner can end sex at any time. **Any person involved can end sex at any time**. You have to listen the entire time because they may want to end it. Even if you are having a great time, you have to stop.

Sex (and bondage) is all about trust.

You never do anything to your partner that they don't want (and you wouldn't them to do to you – unless otherwise agreed upon).

To end sex: Let your partner know you want to stop. Say,

- "Hey, I'm good. Let's take a break."
- "Let's take a timeout"
- "Can we pause?"

You can say anything that lets them know you want to stop. You can say, "stop!"

You can also try some nonverbal stuff:

- Move your body away from them.
- Put your hands up like, "hold up!"

Know you can stop sex at any point.
You don't have to have a reason. You don't have to explain yourself (although, if you plan to have sex with them again, that might help you have better sex in the future.)

Know your partner can stop at any time.
This means you have to listen to your partner during sex. If they seem not into it, you can '**call out the unusual thing,**' and ask them,

> "Hey, you look uninterested/upset/are frowning/scowling, etc. Do you want to keep having sex or change positions or do something else?"

This means your partner might stop the sex even though you were into it. If they do that, stop immediately and see what they want to do. Maybe they want to reposition, maybe they are exhausted, maybe they're not into the sex act you were doing.

It takes two "yes's" to start sex, but only one "no" to end it.

If you are unhappy or about to become unhappy with the sex, it is better for you and your partner if you tell them. Ideally, the sooner the better.

If you are no longer comfortable in a situation you had said "yes" to, say you need to pause or stop. You are encouraged to do this because it means you are respecting yourself.

You or your partner can stop the sex at any time for any reason.

Chapter 16. How to Use a Condom

Condoms work as a barrier to prevent fluids (blood, semen, vaginal fluid) from passing. Condoms come as latex and other types. Typically, people use latex unless someone is allergic to it.

0) Carry condoms in loose bags or pockets - not near your body or in tight pockets. The heat from your body, a tight pocket, or in a bag with heavy stuff could damage the condom or package, making the condom fail to stop STIs.

1) Inspect the condom package for an air bubble. The condom package should have an air pocket and resist pressure when squeezed. A tear or pinhole can damage the condom and make it ineffective.

2) Inspect the condom package for an expiration date – **condoms expire!** Only use condoms before this date; otherwise they denature (break apart like plastic left in the sun during the summer.)

3) Open the condom wrapper and inspect for the condom's roll – **condoms have a direction** – the condom should roll down the penis smoothly – with the roll on the outside of the condom (vs. rolling from the inside out). Think of it like a roll of toilet paper - the condom roll should be on the outside of the condom vs inside - between the wall of the condom and the penis.

4) Pinch the tip of the condom and roll down. The pinched tip is also where the semen will go if the penis ejaculates. It also removes an air pocket that could cause the condom to break during sex.

!!! Practice putting it on yourself or an object !!!

- If you put it on the wrong way initially, throw it away and get another one. Don't just flip it around and use it.
- Don't use two or more condoms at a time. Only use one.
- When using lube, put silicone or water-based lube on the condom. Oil-based can denature/destroy a condom.

Cherry #13, page 17.

Section III: After Sex

Chat, connect, call the next day, let them know if you no longer want to go out.

Chapter 17. Bediquette – How to do Aftercare

Cherry #7 Page 10.

After sex acts, especially after orgasms or a partner wants to stop, a few things can happen:

1) You lie down next to each other, snuggling or spooning, holding each other. You lie together in silence or talk.

2) One or both partners roll over and fall asleep.

3) One partner gets up and leaves.

4) You go do other stuff together.

Talking after sex is known as **pillow talk** because both couples are often lying down in bed with their heads on a pillow, talking. **Snuggling** is lying next to each other in some form of an embrace, often with one partner's head on the other's chest or spooning. **Spooning** is a specific type of snuggling where it looks like two spoons side by side. It's like lying on your side, facing the same direction as your partner while hugging.

Aftercare

Aftercare means holding space (meaning, having time set aside) to connect and come back to reality after having sex. This could be talking and/or snuggling.

Pillow Talk

Couples that pillow talk experience more intimacy and connection (Kruger D, 2011). In my opinion, sometimes the best part of sex or a relationship comes immediately afterwards: the snuggling and talking.

What can you talk about?

- The sex. "What was good?" "What did/didn't you like?"
- Your lives or relationship(s).
- Anything. Politics, religion, family, dreams, goals, expectations.
- Ask what you want to know.

Reflect on the sex

If someone was enthusiastic about sexual activity with you (they consented), then discussing how the sex went is the best way to help you each enjoy your sex in the future.

I was in a relationship for 9 months where my partner wanted more eye contact during our sex. I didn't know until we were breaking up. That lack of communication of wants is on both of us.

Active listening

You ask your partner what they liked and didn't. Listen to what they say. You repeat back what you heard. You allow them the chance to correct what you heard. This is called **active listening**. Do this to confirm you heard correctly and so their need for understanding is met.

- "I heard you say you want more eye contact during missionary position."

Discuss 'off limits' topics while having sex

Debriefing after to talk about any topics that are 'off limits' or a turnoff to a partner:

- "I don't want to talk about problems in our relationship during sex."

Say goodbye or goodnight. This is a kind thing to do.

Conversely, if you spend the night in someone else's bed or place, in the morning if you want to leave before they are awake, **wake them up and say goodbye**, unless they told you don't wake them.

Do get their number/contact info.
If you or they got an STI or pregnant, how would you contact each other? Remember, if you get an STI, you should reach out to all of your recent partners to let them know to get tested (many STIs have no symptoms for a while. They could get injured from the STI and/or spread it to others). If you are pregnant, you may want to contact your partner.

Wet spots – often after sex, you are both sweaty messes and there is a large wet spot in the bed of sweat, vaginal juice, and cum. What do you do? Put a towel over, change the sheets, something else you agree to… It's normal.

Chapter 18. What Comes After Pillow Talk?

Text or call the next day.

Story 9

When I first started having sex, I assumed it was like an interview: if the girl liked it (if I did a good job), she would call me the next day. (Because girls picked, and I (and most of my male friends) would have sex with almost anyone). One day, a girl told me I must not like her because I didn't call after we had sex. I said,

"What? No. I like you. I was waiting for your call."

And that's how I learned many girls expect a call or text after sex.

Point of story: Call or text your partner the day after sex.

Following up throughout the week:
Many people want to text daily, some want to talk daily, some are ok with texts every few days. **Ask your partner how much communication they like and what type (call, text, stop-by, etc.)**

Strong Emotional Attachment (Feelings)

It's normal to feel emotional attachment to whoever you had sex with. Women generally feel this more than men, but that isn't a rule.

In Speed Dating by Yaakov and Sue Deyo, they suggest you wait until marriage to have sex because after you have sex, people get emotionally attached. And, when that happens, they have a harder time thinking as clearly about their partner (Deyo & Deyo, 2002).

When a person has sex, dopamine (the feel-good hormone), oxytocin (the bonding hormone), and vasopressin (the trust hormone) are released. In some people, this can be released in higher doses than others, making it difficult to disconnect feelings from the situation, which can make it more challenging to make an informed decision about a potential partner.

Rejecting or Getting Rejected Directly

If you no longer want to have sex with or hang with someone, letting them know directly is the best approach. You can call, text, or meet in person.

Ghosting (Rejecting Indirectly)

Ghosting is ceasing all contact with someone. People who are ghosted often feel hurt and confused because their needs for shared reality and understanding aren't being met.

Other potential topics of conversation:

Pregnancy Scares – you both fear you have a pregnancy.

STI Scares – you fear you have an STI.

Hanging out again – often you will schedule and spend time together.

Defining the relationship – if you keep hanging out, you discuss and label your relationship (i.e. committed, open, casual, etc.). It's a good space to define the boundaries of the relationship.

Section IV: Other Topics

Chapter 19. Rape

Rape is forced, unwanted sex - usually oral, vaginal, or anal sex. It is related to **sexual assault** which is any forced, unwanted sex action. Either can happen during an initially consensual encounter if one partner says they want to stop, and the other partner doesn't stop. All genders can rape and be raped.

Rape and sexual assault have serious negative consequences. To show that, I offer this post from Reddit, below. Note, multiple readers, including my friends and dad, have told me to include a warning:

!!! WARNING: the following is traumatic, even for a piece on rape!!!

"How is rape traumatic?"
Asked by u/MonkeysDontDance. Answer by (u/bsbbtnh, 2018), quoted directly:
"Think of sex like eating. (Almost) everyone enjoys sex and eating. Think of an attractive person as a big juicy steak. You want that in your mouth. Now imagine if someone forced you to eat that steak when you weren't hungry. Not just sat you down and said eat it, but shoved it down your throat. Hell, maybe they even chew it for you and then force feed you. Not exactly how you want to eat a steak, is it? Would be pretty traumatizing. And that is something you would want to eat, though after that, you may not enjoy steak the same way, ever again.

Now imagine being forced to eat something you don't like. Imagine if you were forced to eat someone's shit. They shove it in your mouth, pushing a whole log down your throat. Put a slimy piece in your mouth and make you chew and swish it around. Stick their ass in your face and have a liquid shit in your mouth. When they are done, the entire inside of your mouth is coated in crap, your face caked in it, your nose filled with the odor.

You can puke up the shit, wash your mouth and face, brush your teeth a hundred times, rub some peppermint oil under your nose, but it isn't going to make you feel like you didn't just eat a couple pounds of shit. No matter what you do, you won't feel 'clean'. The smell of shit will always make you nauseous and bring back horrible memories.

Hell, if you're a guy, just imagine having another guy EDIT: forcefully fuck you in the ass EDIT: without your consent. After he finished, you've got his cum inside you, dripping out, his spit all over your asshole, he's had his tongue down his throat, his facial scruff has scratched up the skin on your face.

And imagine that if/when you tell people, some will always ask questions that seem to put the blame on you, or question the authenticity of your claim. If you want to charge the person, you'll have to go to the police, recount everything that happened, moment to moment, in graphic detail. Then, if it goes to court, you'll have to testify in front of dozens of people, including the guy who raped you, and repeat the same story, while being grilled by the defense attorney, who is trying to rip your testimony apart.

EDIT: Just want to clarify that I'm not homophobic, and that the second last paragraph was meant for straight guys to think about what being violated would be like. My thinking, when writing that, was that some people see rape as little more than a sexual act, and that it should be easy to 'just get over' as though it is a bad experience. So I wanted to describe something that was similar to regular sex, but would, to a straight guy, feel very foreign and violating. Because in many ways, rape is akin to regular sex, it is just the non-consenting part that makes it so impactful.

A lot of people have this idea in their head that most rapes occur in a dark alley, with a knife against your throat, and leaves you bruised and beaten. But the most common perpetrator of rape is someone the victim knows, it happens in a place you're familiar with, and it doesn't always result in physical scars. For some people, they are so wasted/drugged that the moment of rape is a blur, but the most traumatic part is waking up partially naked, with painful genitals, someone's bodily fluids in and on you. It is the experience of pulling yourself together while you try to figure out what happened, walking home in panties that are wet from someone else's enjoyment, checking yourself over, hoping you're not going to get pregnant, not going to get an STI. And just trying to piece things together, and figure out who did this to you."

Chapter 20. Drugs, Alcohol, and Sex

Don't have sex while drunk or high or with people that are drunk or high.

Why? Because:

1) You can't consent while 'messed up' (on mind-altering substances). Which also means your partner can't consent. Which means neither of you have consent to have sex.
2) If you were to start and either of you changed your mind and tried to stop the sex, the partner may not be able to understand that and they may not stop. Or, your partner may ask you to stop and you may not understand that.

Any agreement to have sex while drunk or high is suspect. If someone regrets it the next day, their partner could be convicted of rape or assault.

If you have sex while drunk or high and withdraw consent, your partner may be too high or drunk to understand that and keep going anyway. This is a dangerous and rapey situation.

Having sex while drunk or high is dangerous both morally and legally.

How can you get laid if not during an alcohol/drug-related event?
Meet people wherever, make friends with them, hang out together, don't drink / don't do drugs, ask if they want to kiss.

Chapter 21. FAQ

When are you in a relationship, do you need to be concerned with STIs?

- Sometimes people cheat, and, in my opinion, it's better to get honesty and not get an STI vs. 'fidelity' and end up with dishonesty and an STI.

Sexting

Any image or text you send or upload to the internet on any platform is stored and saved on a database for eternity. Any of those could leak – meaning they could become public without your consent. You could lose your job or some other status, even if you are sexting between consenting adults.

I don't recommend sending nudes.

Proceed knowing the risk that whatever you send may become public at any time.

Don't ever send or request nudes to/from someone under 18. If you're under 18, don't take naked pictures of yourself. Not even if you are legally allowed to consent to sex. Any pictures of a person under 18 are lawfully considered possession of child pornography. Any sending is that plus distribution.

Chapter 22. Communication Moves

If life was a video game, here are some of the moves:

Assume honesty: Don't assume people are playing games with you.

- I like the explanation in Models by Mark Manson published in 2011 on pg 150, "Assume Honesty..." (Manson, 2011). The point is that assuming people are playing games means you will only attract people who are playing games. Assuming honesty attracts honest and forthright people.
- Don't assume people are being sarcastic, which means saying one thing but feeling the opposite. The goal of sarcasm is to mock. Mocking and making fun of someone.

Ask for what you want vs. asking around it.

- "Can you give me a ride to the airport on Saturday at 8am?" instead of "What are you doing Saturday morning?"

Active listening – as discussed earlier in talk during sex and talk after sex.

Nonviolent Communication (NVC).

- In my opinion, one of the best ways to connect.

Here an example of NVC in how to tell someone they smell bad:

- State the observable facts
  - "When you showed up and I could smell your body odor,"
- Say your emotion
  - "I felt turned-off."
- In NVC, say your needs
  - "I have a need for cleanliness."
- In Authentic Relating (a related practice), say what you imagine is going on
  - "What I imagine is happening is you forgot to shower."
- Say your request, something they can do immediately.
  - "Can you take a quick shower?"

Ask what you want to know.

- In my opinion, one of the best ways to connect.

Tell your partner when you are upset with them.

- How else will they know? I like the explanations in this book: Crucial Confrontations (now titled Crucial Accountability) (Patterson, Grenny, McMillan, & Switzler, 2004).

Bad communication moves:

Avoiding talking about things that bother you.

Trying to pressure people to do something.

Demanding people do something

Denying responsibility for your shit.

Judging/comparing – based on morals.

Deserving – assuming people deserve some outcome.

tl;dr

(Too long; didn't read)

Before sex:
Hang out with the person you want to have sex with. If they avoid spending time with you, they probably aren't interested in sexual activity with you. Even if they do spend time with you, you still need to get consent before you hug, kiss, etc.

Before you initiate a kiss (or any sex act), ask the four questions of sexual activity:

- "Do you want to kiss? What sex acts do you want to do?" (Consent)
- "Do you know if you have any STIs? When was the last time you had sex/were tested for STIs?" (Sexually transmitted infection, STIs, check)
- Before vaginal sex, "What birth control are you using? What is your plan if that fails?" (Pregnancy planning)
- "What type of relationship are you looking for?" (Relationship intentions)

You need permission to touch someone. Ask them for permission. Only proceed if they say, "yes." Silence or "maybe" isn't consent. Don't 'just go for it.' Don't just lean in and try to kiss them (or reach out and hug/touch them.)
Every human has the right to decide what happens with their body. If you touch without consent, you are violating that.

STIs:
If they don't have any STI symptoms but have had unprotected sex, they could have an STI. The only way to know is getting tested.

To prevent STI transfer, use a dental dam for vaginal oral sex and a condom for penis oral, vaginal, or anal sex. With condoms, use water or silicone-based lube unless it's oral sex.

If they have an STI (or if you do), you need to talk and think about if you want to proceed. You can do many sex actions without spreading STIs, but some you can't.

Pregnancy planning:
If you don't agree on birth control or what happens if the birth control fails, don't have sex.

Relationship planning:
If you aren't looking for the same type of relationship, don't have sex.

During sex:

- Keep getting consent for each new action and position.
- Especially, always ask and reconfirm consent before engaging in rough sex acts: choking, slapping, hair pulling, hitting, squeezing hard...
- Verbalize your expectations. If you want something, you need to ask for it. Ask them what their expectations, wants, and goals are. Ask with curiosity: which implies you are open to any answer. Ask them how they are doing and what is working.
- Don't assume. Explicit, verbal communication is the best practice to help you both get your needs, desires, and boundaries met.
    - Know you can stop the sex at any time for any reason.
        - If you are no longer comfortable in a situation you had said "yes" to, say you need to pause or stop. You are encouraged to do this because it means you are respecting yourself.
- Use lube.
- During making out (extended kissing), rubbing your hand on their body (non-genital parts) generally increases arousal.
- Before touching genitals or oral sex, touch or kiss on their non-genitals areas. Teasing, touching close to their genitals then moving away, can be hot.

- During vaginal sex, touch the clitoris. All of the nerves are connected, and the pleasure center is there. Touching the clitoris is one way to achieve orgasm during vaginal sex. It is one of the ways to achieve orgasm during vaginal sex. Some women do not need clitoral stimulation to orgasm during sex as penetration alone can stimulate the g-spot and lead to an orgasm that way.
- For anal play, don't just jam stuff into the ass. Apply lots of lube, go slowly, and let the ass relax.

Know that sex takes practice. Sex gets better the more you do it overall and with a consistent person.

People who masturbate usually orgasm and enjoy sex more (because they know how their body works).

After sex:

- Talk.
- Say goodbye or goodnight.
- Call or text the next day.
- If you want a relationship, try to schedule more time to spend together.
- If not, let them know. Don't ghost them (stop replying to them without a text saying you are no longer interested).

Additional Resources:

Consent

Learning Good Consent (Crabb, 2016)

STIs

cdc.gov/STI/default.htm

Herpes Handbook by Terri Warren, R.N., M.S., M.Ed. Nurse Practitioner Published by The PORTLAND PRESS Portland, Oregon Copyright©, 2019

Pregnancy Prevention

Bedsider.org

Relationships

Speed Dating by Deyo 2002

How to do sex acts

The Guide to Getting it On by Paul Joannides

Wiki-how articles

For example, search online "how to grind dance wikihow." Then click the link.

For clitoral stimulation, I recommend (omgyes.com, etc.).

https://www.avert.org/sex-stis/how-to-have-sex/vaginal-sex

General Sex Ed

S.E.X., Second Edition: The All-You-Need-To-Know Sexuality Guide to Get You Through Your Teens and Twenties by Heather Corinna

Doing It by (Witton, 2017)

Gender stuff

My Gender Workbook or Gender Outlaws by Kate Bornstein.

Communication

Nonviolent Communication by Marshall Rosenberg (1999-2015)

Crucial Confrontations: Tools for Resolving Broken Promises, Violated Expectations, and Bad Behavior. Patterson, K., Grenny, J., McMillan, R., & Switzler, A. (2004).

If all else fails, email me: harry@asexed.com I'll answer you or point you to someone that can. Also, searching your question or posting it on the internet should give you some ideas.

Works Cited

Authentic Relating Games Night. (2016). Austin, Tx.

Black Box Improv Classes. (2017). Dayton, Ohio.

Bloom, R. (Director). (2018). *Explained: The Female Orgasm. Season 1 Episode 16.* [Motion Picture].

Carnegie, D. (1936). *How to Win Friends & Influence People.* Simon & Schuster.

Crabb, C. (2016). *Learning Good Consent.* AK Press.

Deyo, Y., & Deyo, S. (2002). *Speed Dating: The Smarter, Faster Way to Lasting Love.*

Dickson, M. (1996). *A Woman's Worst Nightmare.* Retrieved from No Safe Place: Violence Against Women: https://www.pbs.org/kued/nosafeplace/articles/nightmare.html

Dobkin, D. (Director). (2005). *Wedding Crashers* [Motion Picture].

House of Bacchus . (2018). Consent Class. *Trauma* . Columbus.

Hughes, S. M. (2007). Sex differences in romantic kissing among college students: An evolutionary perspective. *Evolutionary Psychology,* 5(3), 612-631.

Joannides, P. (2017-2018). *Guide to Getting It On!*

Kruger D, H. H. (2011). Tendencies to fall asleep first after sex are associated with greater partner desires for bonding and affection. *Journal of Social, Evolutionary, and Cultural Psychology, 5*(4), 239-247. Retrieved from (2011). Tendencies to fall asleep first after sex are associated with greater partner desires for bonding and affection. Journal of Social, Evolutionary, and Cultural Psychology, 5(4), 239-247. http://dx.doi.org/10.1037/h009: http://psycnet.apa.org/fulltext/2012-24854-004.html

Laskowski, C. (Producer). (2018). *Explained: The Female Orgasm, Season 1 Episode 16* [Motion Picture].

Manson, M. (2011). *Models: Attract Women through Honesty.*

Orgasmic Meditation. (2016).

Patterson, K., Grenny, J., McMillan, R., & Switzler, A. (2004). *Crucial Confrontations: Tools for Resolving Broken Promises, Violated Expectations, and Bad Behavior.*

Rawji, N. (2016, August 16). Retrieved from https://twitter.com/thatxxv/status/765559476694847488

SOPP, A. (2018). *Antioch SOPP*. Retrieved from (https://www.antiochcollege.edu/campus-life/residence-life/health-safety/sexual-offense-prevention-policy-title-ix)
u/bsbbtnh. (2018, March). *morbidquestions*. Retrieved from Reddit (Used with permission): https://www.reddit.com/r/morbidquestions/comments/81qo8w/how_is_rape_traumatic/dv4kuxm
Vogel, L. (2015). Rethink weight limits on morning-after pill. *Canadian Medical Association Journal*, 719–720.
Welz, L. (1982-2000). *Cherry.* Last Gasp.
Witton, H. (2017). *Doing it.*

About the people who worked on this book:

Harry Lindner, likes to start things to solve problems. That's included:

- two local chapters of Authentic Relating (an emotional intelligence/communication groups in Columbus and Dayton, Oh).
- this book, which he started in the summer of 2010, was an app in 2013, and he has been working on (and off) for the past 9 years.
- a DIY forum + calendar and a potluck Shabbat group in 2009 and 2010.
- a student activist group and a Shabbat service during undergrad.
- a political discussion club and raise awareness about Darfur campaign while he was in high school.

Harry has a few other ideas to improve the world and help people, including a list of world problems and a search engine/database of metadata for movies. A draft version of that search engine sits here:
https://github.com/hlindwin/moviesearch.

Harry works a day job as a database developer (writing SQL and python). Outside of that, he takes improv classes, participates in a Nonviolent Communication group, swing dances, attends and occasionally helps at a Shabbat dinner group called Havayah, and plays League of Legends (a platinum Sona main (before she was popular as a carry). He also hangs with friends, family, and hikes around town. His favorite color is green. :-)

He grew up in the Midwest: Cincinnati, Ohio and still splits his time there and Columbus, Ohio. His parents were both nurses. He has a Master's in Nuclear Engineering and a Master's in Public Policy from University of Texas at Austin, and a Bachelor's in Psychology from Ohio State University.

Harry's previous publications include a Diablo II strategy guide on diabloii.net and meta-analysis of uranium recovery from seawater published in Energy Economics.

Harry identifies as male, his genitals match his gender identity, and he was assigned male at birth. He mostly has had female presenting partners.

Julie DiNuoscio, MA, LPC: Empathic connection has always been a high priority in her life. The desire to feel known is so ingrained in who we are as humans, and she is passionate about helping others to feel known by others, but to also know themselves better too. Loving and appreciating ourselves does not come naturally as a culture, and she wants to foster a space in which we learn to embrace all of who we are.

Be Known, her therapy practice, was birthed from the deep desires expressed by many clients. Many individuals expressed not knowing much about their bodies or sexual selves. Many couples expressed the desire to feel seen, heard, and known by their partner. Even more expressed little connection to their inner self and the emotions warring within. Therefore, her goal became to help others feel known.

While she has a personal philosophy, her training influences the path that she takes to help clients through their healing. She graduated from Miami University in 2015 with a Bachelor's in Psychology and received her Master of Arts in Counseling in 2017 from Cincinnati Christian University. She welcomes all into her space, whatever their background.

She has spent time working for a non-profit teaching students about sex and relationships as well as worked in various private practice settings with both couples and individuals. She grew up in Cincinnati, a town that is known for being rather conservative. She has witnessed friends, family, and strangers experience shame, pain, embarrassment, and more because of the taboo stigma that accompanies sex. No matter what part of the United States you might find yourself in, people are still struggling to talk about this beautiful and life-giving (literally!) act. She is passionate about helping break down the walls of discomfort and shame and working to open people up to talking about sex. She believes that education can bring about great change and she would love to see people stop settling for mediocre and step into the fullness of their own potential. It is clear to her that educating others about their bodies decreases shame and opens up conversations around self-love, consent, and healthy boundaries. She has so many friends tell her she's the first person to teach them what a clitoris is, or that it's normal for sex to not last for hours like in porn, or that sex isn't supposed to hurt... ever! Her hope is that by providing a safe space for people to begin having discussions about sex, we can slowly see change to where people are comfortable with their sexuality and they are empowered to make healthy choices for themselves and their bodies, based on empirically supported research.

For fun, she enjoys dancing, reading fiction novels, playing guitar, traveling, and spending time with loved ones. Having a healthy work-life balance is important to her and she enjoy creating space for herself to breathe and live life to the fullest.

Allison Schottenstein, is from Cincinnati, Ohio, but she has been around the world. She went to Brandeis University for her undergraduate, where she majored in Judaic Studies and Women and Gender Studies. After college, she decided to continue her studies at the University of Texas at Austin. She has a MA and Ph.D. in American History with subspecialties in Race/Ethnic, American and European Jewish History, and Civil Rights.

At the University of Texas at Austin, she became involved in the Symposium on Women, Gender, and Sexuality to help educate people about gender and sexuality throughout history. She has a first-level certificate from ATIXA in Title IX. Allison has numerous publications. She has taught at the University of Cincinnati, University of Cincinnati Blue Ash, and Cincinnati State Technical and Community College. Her decision to become involved in this project stems from her concern that people are having sex ill-informed. Many of us are clueless about having sex and what consent means. She wants to spread the word that good sex is only between consenting partners. Allison wants to be part of the movement to change the way we teach sex education. She fundamentally believes this book will provide a platform to the sexually curious seeking a sexually satisfying, stimulating, safe, sexual life.

Sharon Welz, "A jack of all trades and a master of none." Her most important job is to be the cleaner. They always say cleanliness is next to Godliness. God is love to her. She has been a teacher, nurse, costumer, builder of the Roswell Spacewalk, and owner of a sign shop. She was born in Brooklyn, New York on July 21, 1949. Moved to southern California in the year 1959 to become a valley girl. Being transported to California was like another planet, but she loved it. The smell of all the blossoms filled the air.

In 1969, the moon landing on July 20, one day before her July 21. It was another amazing moment in her life. We were ready to fly. You started then slowly all the magic and love that had started from that moment. Now at 70, after celebrating landing on the moon 50 years ago, she sits here saddened by the facts that we had 2 mass shootings in one evening, and we have had 255 mass shootings in this year alone.

On July 4 weekend, she started a portal of love, hoping to bring the message out to the world, one step at a time, but if we don't take the giant leap forward, she just doesn't know.

With Cherry and other people, Larry Welz and Sharon Welz want to bring LOVE AND SEX together. It doesn't matter your sex, color, gender, or wherever you came from LOVE is the answer. Let's do it together. She believes that Cherry illustrates sex and love which are the two components of a healthy sex relationship.

Love and Sex. Since her first experience with sex was so exciting, she knew then there needed to be better teachings about sex. She notes all get mixed messages. Sex can be one of the most rewarding moments in your life as long as it's given with love. Sex without love is what rashes us all to become negative in our behavior. Never let yourself become the victim always be empowered.

She and Larry are now proud of the fact that Harry Linder has included Cherry to illustrate the pleasures of SEX and LOVE thru Cherry's antics brought to you since 1982.

Larry Welz, comic creator, was born & raised in Bakersfield, California, where he did theatre in High School. In 1967 or so, he hitched a ride north to San Francisco where the so-called Underground Comix movement was getting under way. His work in such comic books as Yellow Dog, Bakersfield Kountry Komics, Funnybook, San Francisco Comic Book, Captain Guts, and Cherry Poptart is an important, if obscure, part of comic book history. He continued doing Cherry Comics, a spicy, satirical take on the Wacky Teenager comics that were popular in the 50s & 60s, while living in Northern California.

Mr. Welz later moved to Roswell, New Mexico, where he & his wife Sharon owned & operated a sign shop, Signs of Life in Roswell, for ten years or so, during which time they built a roadside attraction, The Roswell Spacewalk http:// www.roswellspacewalk.com/,an immersive walk-through blacklight art installation, which recounted the Roswell Incident & projected viewers through time & space.

Mr. Welz also painted carnival rides; funhouses, darkrides, mirror mazes & the occasional freak show banners for many years.

Mr. & Mrs. Welz now live in Albuquerque, New Mexico, where he has recommenced writing & drawing Cherry Comics.

Cherrycomix.com

Cherry #17 page 22.

Printed in Great Britain
by Amazon

40069761R00067